"I'm get... ... ... just not right."

"Getting married to Neil is just not right, you mean."

"And who are you to judge? I bet you've never wanted to marry anyone in your life."

"Neither have you," said Ewan quietly.

He reached up to Caron's heavy mass of hair and slowly ran his fingers through it. "Don't," she said, shivering.

"Marrying a man you don't love is fairly despicable, wouldn't you say?"

Sally Carr trained as a journalist and has worked on several national newspapers. She was brought up in the West Indies and her travels have taken her nearly all over the world, including Tibet, Russia and North America. She lives with her husband, two dogs, three goldfish and six hens in an old hunting lodge in Northamptonshire, and has become an expert painter and decorator. She enjoys walking, gardening and playing the clarinet.

Rebel Bride
Sally Carr

Harlequin Books

TORONTO • NEW YORK • LONDON
AMSTERDAM • PARIS • SYDNEY • HAMBURG
STOCKHOLM • ATHENS • TOKYO • MILAN
MADRID • WARSAW • BUDAPEST • AUCKLAND

ISBN 0-373-17324-5

REBEL BRIDE

First North American Publication 1997.

CHAPTER ONE

THE man behind the bar looked at her in astonishment and repeated, 'You want to go to Ewan Cameron's place?'

'Of course I want to go there,' said Caron stiffly. 'I just said so, didn't I?' The flight from London, coupled with a two-hour bus ride, had been exhausting and the man's look of amazement and sly appraisal would have been enough to try anyone's patience. 'I was told you ran a taxi service,' she said. 'Will you take me?'

The man blinked. 'Me? Now? Take you to Ewan Cameron?'

'Is there anyone else who could take me?' enquired Caron as patiently as she could. What was the matter with this man?

He shrugged. 'I guess I thought you had a car. It's kinda late to be going visiting at this time of night.'

'I'm not paying a social call. It's purely business,' Caron replied, adding with a sarcasm she couldn't resist, 'If that's all right with you, of course.'

The man lifted his hands placatingly. 'No offence, OK? You just gave me a shock, that's all. I can't see Ewan welcoming visitors at the moment. But if it's business...' He fell silent, staring at her briefcase.

Caron could feel the waves of tiredness seeping over her. The travelling she had done in the last twenty-four hours had nearly drained her. And her last-minute plan to come out here seemed rather over the top now.

All she wanted to do was lie down and sleep somewhere, instead of having to deal with this rather dopey-
seeming bartender in what appeared to be nothing more
than a one-horse town in the middle of the Canadian
Rockies.

'Is there something wrong with Mr Cameron?' she demanded as coolly as she could.

'Wrong with him?' said the barman, coming round
from behind the counter. 'There's nothing wrong with
him,' he added in surprise. 'Best horseman this town's
ever seen. It's just—'

'Don't tell me,' interrupted Caron hastily. 'It's just
that he doesn't have much time for visitors, right?'

'Well . . .' began the barman and Caron sighed. At this
rate they'd be here all night. They really ought to get a
move on, but there was so much about this whole
business that she simply didn't know.

She pushed a hand distractedly through her hair. She
really shouldn't have gone off from London at half cock
like that. If the truth be told she had only the barest
idea what this business with Ewan Cameron was all
about. It was so unprofessional to be this unprepared,
so unlike anything she had ever done before.

She swallowed, and shook her head as if that would
somehow clear her brain. The illuminated sign adver-
tising a well-known brand of beer which hung over the
bar was also a clock and its hands stood at a little after
eight.

She sighed. Eight p.m. here; three a.m. in Britain. No
wonder she felt so unglued. She rubbed her eyes and
realised the barman was still watching her, taking in her
smart business suit, her thick golden hair swept severely
off her pale oval face.

'Well,' she said, making an effort to sound bright and efficient, 'I think we ought to make a start, don't you? I'm sorry you think Mr Cameron's too shy to meet me, but my business really is most urgent. The poor old man probably goes to bed quite early and I wouldn't like to arrive there too late. I shouldn't like to get him up.'

The barman was staring at her as if she had turned into a visitor from Mars. Perhaps this place was such a backwoods that all the inhabitants had gone slightly mad. She looked at him in exasperation. 'Do you think we could make a start?' she repeated.

He jerked to life as if he had been given electric-shock treatment. 'Yes ma'am. Right away.' He thought of what was up in the hills waiting for them. This was one fare he would not have missed for the world. 'You got bags?'

'A small one,' said Caron. 'It's outside.'

He nodded. 'OK. There's just one thing.' He hesitated. 'I guess you never met Mr Cameron, huh?'

'No,' admitted Caron. 'I haven't, but so what? He's hardly going to bite me, is he?'

He smiled apologetically at her. 'No ma'am. I guess not. I just—'

'Well?' demanded Caron exasperatedly. 'What is it?'

He shrugged again and looked rather sheepishly at her. 'I do rooms here if he tells you to go to hell.'

The taxi trip was the most difficult journey of all the ones that Caron had endured in the previous few hours. The warmth from the heater lapped around her, tempting her into the shallows of a sleep that she wanted to sink into completely.

Unfortunately the suspension didn't work as well as the heater. Twice she found herself catapulting into the roof. The cheap plastic of the seat suck to her hands

and the air smelt of stale cigarette smoke. Her mouth
was dry and her eyes hurt. This was what hell was like—
jiggling endlessly along an unmade road in a car driven
by someone who was a bit dim to say the least.

He was probably driving her around in circles, she
thought grimly, while poor Mr Cameron was no doubt
sitting up way past his bedtime and worrying himself
sick over what had happened to her.

However, it soon became obvious that the barman,
for all his little peculiarities, was not driving her around
in circles. Up and up they went into the mountains, until
the road almost disappeared as a dirt track into the forest.

'Just about here, I guess,' he muttered as he swung
right into a driveway she hadn't noticed and up a much
smoother track to a long, low building which seemed,
in the fast-fading light, to be set in the very mountains
themselves.

The car stopped and the driver flicked a glance at her.
Why did he seem so nervous? 'Well, we're here,' he said
hurriedly. 'I'll just get your bag.'

'There doesn't seem to be anybody about,' said Caron
doubtfully, handing him the fare. 'Are you sure we've
come to the right place?'

'Positive,' he nodded. 'Why don't you just try
knocking? Maybe Ewan Cameron's got hard of hearing
in his old age.'

Caron looked suspiciously at him. What was the
matter with the man? She could have sworn he was
laughing at her, but she was simply too tired to bother
cross-questioning him. 'All right,' she said. 'I will. Thank
you for getting my bag.'

She pushed open the sagging car door and made her
way to the ranch house with an effort. The cool night

air was wonderful after that stuffy taxi and she felt her spirits rising. This was all just as she'd pictured it.

The house was solidly built out of stone, with a wooden veranda running the whole way across the front. Her footsteps sounded hollow on its boards, and she began to feel her first serious doubts about what she had done. Why had no one come out to meet them? Surely Mr Cameron hadn't really gone to bed already?

The door opened just as she raised her hand to knock on it and, astonished by the man standing on the threshold, her hand stayed aloft, as though she were back in school and trying to grab the teacher's attention.

This could not possibly be Ewan Cameron. The man she had begun to picture in her mind was a frail old little pensioner who was going to be so pleased that she had called.

But the man standing in front of her was only about thirty-five, well over six feet and broad with it. His face was strong-featured, framed by shaggy brown hair. And his eyes, the deepest blue eyes Caron had ever seen outside of her own mirror, were staring straight at her.

They dropped to her smart court shoes and travelled slowly up her well-cut silk suit, missing nothing out. In astonishment she realised that she was staring at him just as closely and then, as their eyes met again, she felt the need to break the silence between them—to say something, anything at all, to break the sudden tension holding them in thrall.

But before she could say anything he spoke. 'You got a question?' he said laconically, a spark of humour flaring far away in his eyes at her upraised arm.

'Ewan Cameron?' she attempted, her hand flopping limply to her side, the words coming out as a croak. No wonder the taxi driver had found her expectation of a frail old man so funny.

He looked past her to the taxi and then focused again on her face. 'That's me,' he replied. 'Can I help you?'

His expression was guarded but Caron took courage from the easy politeness of his words.

'I'm Caron Lane,' she said breathlessly. 'Sorry I'm so late.'

His eyebrows lifted, but he said nothing, continuing to watch her closely, waiting for her to make the next move.

She looked at him in growing exasperation. She could hardly demand that he let her in, but she was damned if she was going to stand out there all night. 'It is rather cold out here,' she said pointedly.

Ewan nodded. 'It gets that way up here at this time of year.' Caron took a grip on her mounting infuriation. Something in this man's eyes told her that he was not one to be pushed about.

He folded his arms and leant comfortably against the doorjamb. 'You'll find it much warmer in the taxi,' he said with a laugh in his eyes that made her suddenly want to kick him in the shins.

'Don't you know who I am?' she demanded.

'No,' he said simply. He looked back over her shoulder at the taxi and a small smile twisted his lips. 'But if you're a travelling saleswoman you have come to the wrong address. I'm not buying anything tonight.'

'Saleswoman?' echoed Caron. 'Mr Cameron, I—'

He lifted his hand. 'Some other time,' he said. 'I'd love to hear your sales pitch, but not tonight. It must be quite something, though, if you can afford to hire a taxi for your appointments.'

His voice was light, mocking, but before Caron could think of a suitably crushing reply he continued, 'What's your speciality? Encyclopaedias, vacuum cleaners, insurance...?' He paused and let his eyes linger over her body once more. 'Or are you selling something else entirely?'

Caron coloured angrily at his only too obvious meaning. 'Are you as insulting as this to everyone you meet?' she demanded hotly.

He nodded slowly. 'Mostly,' he agreed. And then, smiling straight into her eyes, he added, 'But I can be a lot worse if I really try. Depends on how creative I'm feeling.'

Caron swallowed. 'Mr Cameron,' she began, 'I—'

But he was staring past her now, as if she didn't exist, at the taxi driver, who was leaning against the car door. 'Why I should have thought you would have known better, Sam, I don't know,' he called out. 'But you can take her back into town now. If this stunt was a welcome-home joke from the rest of boys, you can tell them I was truly gratified and I'll buy them all a beer when I see them next.'

Sam opened his mouth, closed it again, took two steps towards the house and then stopped as Caron turned to glare at him. 'You can get in your taxi for the moment, thank you, Sam,' she said icily. 'I have some business to discuss with Mr Cameron.'

She turned back to Ewan and tried hard to steady her voice as she looked up into the unfathomable blue depths of his eyes. 'I may as well make it clear that I am neither a joke nor a travelling saleswoman, Mr Cameron. You will no doubt have received my letter explaining my presence here. I apologise for arriving this late in the evening but my plane was delayed. I am Caron Lane, the solicitor.'

She held out her hand and he looked down gravely at her for a second before his long brown fingers enclosed hers.

'Caron Lane, the solicitor, huh?' he said. 'Well, ma'am, I have to admit I've never heard of you, although you sound a long way from home.'

'London, actually,' she replied automatically, her frostiness thawing slightly at the use of the word 'ma'am', before she looked at him in dawning horror, her hand still in his. 'Never heard of me?' she repeated slowly.

There was more than a hint of amusement in his eyes now. 'Must be a dent to your ego, huh? All that soliciting and a guy like me has no idea who you are.'

She pulled her fingers away from his and shook her head angrily. 'Don't be so silly,' she said. 'Of course you've heard of me. I know that my firm has already written to you about the arrangements for my visit.

'Unfortunately the man who should have been coming to see you—my father—is recovering from a heart attack, so I've come in his place. I know you were asked to make a hotel reservation for him to allow time for him to discuss your inheritance, so I'll just take it over, if that's all right. It was all such a rush that, as I explained, I didn't really expect you to be able to reply in time.'

Ewan shook his head with barely concealed impatience. 'I didn't get any letter. And none of my relatives has died recently.'

Caron shied involuntarily at his dismissive tone. Perhaps this hadn't been such a good idea after all. 'But—' she began.

'Lady,' he said, 'you are seriously beginning to try my patience. Now, how much did they pay you?'

'Pay me?' faltered Caron. 'Who?'

'Sam and the rest of the guys,' replied Ewan. 'I guess you must be one of those strippergram girls. You've certainly got the figure for it, but whatever they paid you I'll double it for you to go away now. It's my first night home and I don't need this.'

He turned as if to go and she reached out and caught him by the elbow. 'What you need at the moment is a punch on the nose,' she snapped. 'Even if I was a...a—' she blushed furiously '—a strippergram,' she forced out, 'I would need my head examined if I was going to take my clothes off for money in this temperature.'

He raised his eyebrows mockingly. 'You mean you'd do it for free?'

She wrenched her hand from his sleeve as if it were burning her. 'I meant nothing of the sort,' she spat.

'Look,' he said more gently. 'I am sorry if I've misjudged you, but if you think I'm going to fall for some story about an inheritance you are way off line. Now, it's getting late and I'd be obliged if you got back in that taxi and took off back to town and whoever put you up to this stunt before I seriously decide to lose my temper.'

They stared at each other for a long moment and then Caron, her eyes sparking, opened her handbag, extracted a piece of paper and thrust it under his nose.

'Here, read this,' she snapped. 'It's a copy of the letter I sent you, informing you of the alterations. If you care to doubt my credentials you are of course at liberty to call my London office.'

There was a split-second when she thought he was just
going to tear up the piece of paper she had handed him,
and, tilting her chin, she mentally dared him to just try.

Then, his lips twisting at her obstinacy, Ewan un-
folded the letter and read it in the light streaming out
of the open door. When he got to the bottom his eyebrows came together in one black line. His eyes flicked
up to Caron and then across to Sam, who was trying
very hard, without the least success, to look as though
he was not drinking in every word that was being said.

'Sam?' called Ewan.

'Yes?'

'I don't think the lady will be requiring your services
again tonight.'

'Now just hold on,' remonstrated Caron. 'I'll need to
go back to town.'

Ewan's eyes stared down at hers. 'When you do, I'll
take you. But for now you'd better come in,' he said,
picking up her bag and waiting for her to enter his home
before following her in and booting the door closed
behind them.

Sam, left scratching his head in the middle of the yard,
shrugged helplessly, and when, after a few minutes,
nothing happened he got into his car and started the
engine. A long, long time ago he'd promised himself
never to be surprised by what Ewan Cameron did. And
once again he'd broken that promise, he thought as he
drove away down the mountain and back to town.

There was no hallway in the house; the door led straight
into a big, comfortable sitting room. Caron walked into
the middle of it, before she turned to face Ewan.

'That was pretty high-handed of you, wasn't it?' she
demanded. 'I would have been perfectly happy to pay

Sam's waiting time, and he offered me a room at his bar.'

'I wouldn't let a dog sleep in one of his rooms,' said Ewan, dumping her bag down.

It was difficult to tear her eyes away from him, the relaxed, unhurried way he moved, his faded jeans and plaid shirt emphasising his big, well-muscled body.

As his eyes met hers she knew he was acutely aware of the way she was staring at him. She began to blush furiously. This was ridiculous. She was here purely on business and in a week's time it would be her wedding day. It was unthinkable that she could be so attracted to another man within five minutes of meeting him.

Hurriedly she turned her back on him and took a step towards the big stone fireplace, holding out her hands to the small fire flickering in the log-burning stove.

'Something wrong?' he said in his slow, soft drawl.

'No,' she replied quickly. 'Nothing at all. Absolutely nothing. I was just, er, admiring your fireplace.'

He was walking up behind her now. She could feel the hairs on the back of her neck prickling and she swallowed, realising suddenly that as far as she knew she was all alone with this man in a strange house, thousands of miles from home.

She should never have had that blazing row with Neil, never have come here in the first place, and certainly never have let the taxi driver go back to town.

But now was no time to show fear. She looked down at the crackling logs and said the first thing that came into her head. 'So nice to see a real fire. I live in a smokeless zone, you know.'

She was babbling and she knew it, but she couldn't seem to stop. 'My fiancé has one of those pretend fires—

powered by gas, and awfully good-looking, but there's no real warmth.'

'Is that a description of your fiancé?' drawled Ewan.

Caron spun round to face him. 'Don't you know how to do anything but insult people?'

'Oh, I know how to do lots of things, Caron.' The loaded meaning of his words and use of her first name gave her a thrill of intimacy she hadn't expected. Then anger at how he was so easily keeping her off balance flooded through her.

'You're standing too close to me,' she said with an effort.

He cocked an eyebrow. 'You got one of those five-mile exclusion zones?'

She remembered the classes in assertiveness training she had attended. 'You are invading my personal space,' she said as firmly as she could.

He stared down at her for a long moment. 'This house is my personal space, Caron. You're the one who's doing the invading.'

'I've come here on business,' she insisted. 'Did you really not get my letter?'

He turned and walked over to a cupboard. 'No, I didn't. First I knew was when you turned up tonight and thrust that copy of it under my nose. As to my "inheritance", as you call it, all I can remember about my second cousin are my mother's tales about him being a hopeless alcoholic. And that was a long, long time ago. So I can't see that anything he would have bothered to leave me is worth the beermat it was probably written on.'

'My firm does not conduct its business on beermats,' said Caron stiffly.

He looked back at her. 'Maybe you should,' he said. 'It might have stopped you from getting so pompous.'

'I'm not pompous,' she snapped. 'I'm trying to be businesslike.'

'Well, don't,' he said. 'It'll bring me out in a rash.'

'Oh, yes,' agreed Caron caustically. 'That would be a terrible thing. I mean, if you're going to be rich you don't want to be spotty.'

He grinned slowly at her gibe and then, with a studied mischievous look on his face, said, 'Has your fiancé ever told you that you have great legs?'

Caron's mouth fell open at his challenging look and then, trying to regain some sort of calmness, she snapped, 'I hardly think my fiancé's opinions about my legs are relevant.'

'What about the other bits of you?' asked Ewan innocently. 'Or do you tell him they're not relevant to him either?'

'I don't—' began Caron, and then she stopped and took a deep breath. How could she allow a complete stranger to bait her like this?

'That's not what I meant at all, and you know it,' she forced out as calmly as she could. 'You're simply twisting my words.'

'Oh,' he replied, his expression deadpan. 'And I thought that was a lawyer's speciality.'

She clenched her teeth as Ewan gazed at her, a little smile playing on his much too handsome face.

'I meant—' she began, but he was too quick for her.

'You meant of course that while you're out of his sight you become the original prim virgin who doesn't allow anyone to discuss her legs.'

Caron took a deep breath. This man was absolutely impossible. 'Mr Cameron...' she began.

'Call me Ewan,' he told her. 'Where is he, anyway?'

'Who?' she asked, bewildered by his sudden question.

'Your fiancé. Remember him?'

'Of course I remember him,' she retorted. 'He...' She paused. 'Neil is in London, if you must know.'

She lifted her chin and looked at him directly. 'Is there any other information you require about my private life, Mr Cameron?' She had wanted the chilliness in her words to slap him down but he refused to be fazed. 'So when's your wedding?' he asked.

'Next Saturday,' she answered shortly. 'Now, do you think we could stop discussing me and—?'

'You really are devoted to duty, aren't you?' he said softly, the sarcasm only too apparent in his words. 'Guess I should be flattered by your coming all the way out here to talk about a bequest when you could be at home in London telling good old Neil just how relevant he's going to be.'

He watched two angry spots of colour begin to flame on her cheeks and then, turning, opened the cupboard door. 'You look like you could use a drink. Want one?'

Caron felt the effect of all the weary hours she had been travelling wash over her in one numbing tidal wave. 'I'd love a cup of tea,' she managed.

He flashed a glance at her. 'Tea?'

'It's very refreshing,' she quavered. 'Especially when you're tired.'

He took a bottle and two glasses from the cupboard and turned back towards her. 'How long have you been travelling?' he asked.

Caron gripped the high mantelpiece for support. 'I don't really know any more,' she said, trying hard, without much success, to sound matter-of-fact. 'The time-difference becomes really confusing after a while.

I took off from Heathrow about one-ish and we eventually got to Calgary about two in the morning British time, although it was only early evening here.

'Then when I was in the coffee-shop someone stole my purse. Luckily I had some cash in the side-pocket of my handbag but I didn't have enough to hire a car so I had to get the bus to town and that took hours. And then I got the taxi here and—' She stopped and shrugged helplessly.

'Why don't you sit down?' he said gently.

Caron glanced at the big red sofa by the fire and thought about how she needed to retain some sort of professional image in front of this deeply disconcerting man. She didn't move.

'It's very comfortable,' he prompted.

Her last bit of resolve crumbling, she sat. The sofa was old and a bit threadbare in places but she sank with a sigh into the soft, deep cushions. Her eyes closed and then, suddenly, flicked open again.

Ewan was sitting beside her. And his closeness was tautening every nerve-ending in her body. He held out a glass to her and she took it.

'I'm right out of tea,' he said as she sipped at the unfamiliar alcohol, the fumes seeming to reach right into her brain. 'Although if it's that miraculous a liquid I could use some myself right now,' he added. 'Unfortunately, bourbon will have to do instead. Drink it, and let's get this business over with.'

Caron looked at him over the rim of her glass and wondered how she was going to admit to this man that she probably knew less about this bequest than he did. What was it that old Mr Benton had told her while her father was convalescing?

'Mr Cameron,' she began, with more confidence than she felt, 'this matter is quite complex. I know I came barging up from town to see you, but I thought you would be expecting me, would have some sort of accommodation arranged. Can't you take me back into town and we can discuss it tomorrow while I try to arrange some sort of transportation back to Calgary?'

He looked at her. 'And just how do you propose to pay for staying at Sam's?'

'I'll pay him tomorrow, after I've been to the bank,' said Caron. 'It's perfectly simple.'

'Sam likes cash on the nail, up front,' said Ewan. 'Besides, it's Sunday tomorrow and Queen Victoria's birthday the day after that.'

Caron stared at him. 'Queen Victoria's birthday?' she repeated incredulously. 'What has that got to do with anything?'

His eyes glinted with amusement. 'It's a national holiday,' he said. 'And the bank in town is closed.'

Caron's jaw dropped. 'But I've got to get back,' she muttered. 'I have so much to sort out.' The little speech she had been psyching herself up to tell Neil burned in her brain. She bit her lip.

'There's no other way,' she said at last, making her mind up. 'I'll stay here tonight and then you can drive me to Calgary tomorrow. I will send you whatever I owe you for petrol and so forth and I shall, of course, make it worth your while.'

There was that look of mocking amusement on his face again. As if a mouse he had caught had told him to get the cheeseboard and make it snappy.

'You know,' he said gently, 'I was under the impression that if you wanted somebody to give you something you said please and hoped for the best.'

Caron blinked and began to realise, with icy clarity, that her habit of demanding what she wanted was not going to get her anywhere with this man. She swallowed. 'I'm sorry,' she muttered. 'I just thought it was the most practical way out of a mess.'

He got up in one fluid movement and looked down at her. 'Well, you thought wrong. In the first place, there's nowhere for you to sleep. I've only just returned myself after a few months away and my usual house-keeper has quit.'

'I can guess why,' flared Caron. 'She probably wasn't very good at brushing off your insults.'

'You're the one who should have majored in those, Caron,' he said softly.

She looked at him as coolly as she could. 'Mr Cameron, much as I hate imposing on your privacy, you also seem to think it impossible for me to stay in town tonight.'

He looked sideways at her. 'I said I didn't think it was a good idea to stay at Sam's. There are other places.'

'But I have no cash left,' she almost wailed. 'The thief took nearly everything, including my traveller's cheques. Look,' she said, trying desperately to hang onto her cool outward shell, 'I have absolutely no objection to sleeping on the sofa. But if you have no housekeeper why can't I sleep in her room?'

A sudden wicked impulse for revenge rushed through her. 'That is, providing she wasn't sleeping with you, of course.'

He gave her a look that was completely unreadable.

'I came all this way to give you some really good news,' she burst out. 'Anybody would think you didn't give a damn about becoming rich overnight.'

His lips parted, as if he was about to say something, and then, a sudden glint of humour flaring in his eyes, he sat down again and leaned comfortably back among the cushions. Caron found herself gazing at the length of his legs and the way his shirt skimmed the muscles in his arms.

She could feel the warmth from his body and wondered what it would be like to feel that warmth next to her skin, to feel his arms around her...

She shook her head impatiently. It was no good thinking like this. She might be feeling rather unbalanced because of what was happening with Neil, but she didn't need to lose her head completely.

There was a mocking expression on Ewan's face. Did he know what she was thinking? She felt her face begin to flame but he just took a quick gulp of his drink and then said, 'OK, Caron, let's hear it. Just how incredibly rich am I going to be?'

CHAPTER TWO

CARON sipped some of the bourbon in her glass and tried not to choke on the pungent oily fumes. 'Well, perhaps not incredibly rich,' she said cautiously, attempting to remember something—anything—that old Mr Benton had told her about this bequest.

If only she had paid more attention. But it was hard to concentrate on anything now, especially in the weeks since Neil had dropped his bombshell.

'I mean,' she explained, hoping desperately that she had got her facts right, 'you won't be able to splash out on a garage full of Ferraris, but it will allow you a much higher standard of living than the one you have at present.'

'Really,' said Ewan softly.

Caron shifted uncomfortably. 'I didn't mean that you're living in a hovel at the moment,' she struggled. 'It's a very nice house... Well, a bit dusty, here and there...' She stopped awkwardly.

What was it that Ewan had said about being away? Where had he been that his home should have got this dilapidated? A sudden vision of him in a jail cell rose up in her mind and she thrust it away with an effort. What on earth was the matter with her? 'I meant—' she began again.

'Caron,' Ewan interrupted.

'Yes?' she said glumly.

He flashed a smile at her. 'When you're in a hole, stop digging.'

She gazed at him silently. He chinked his glass against hers and then said, quite out of the blue, 'What are you really doing here?'

'I told you,' she said as forcefully as she could. 'This is a business trip.'

Ewan stared at her consideringly. 'My long-lost English cousin has finally died, probably of drink, and I stand to inherit his empty whisky bottles.

'It's such an important inheritance that some fancy law firm based in...' he took the letter from his shirt pocket and scanned it again '... in Fleet Street, London EC1, decided to send one of their solicitors—who's just about to get married—all the way out here to tell me about it. Why didn't you just write?'

Caron's heart gave a sudden thud. This man was too shrewd by half. 'Just as well we didn't write,' she said, 'considering you don't seem to have got the last letter.'

He shrugged. 'I'll pick it up next time I go to the post office in town. I don't get regular deliveries.'

His hand circled her wrist and he took the glass from her fingers, setting it on the floor. 'Now. Are you going to tell me exactly what you're doing here? Or am I going to have to make some uncomfortable guesses?'

The pressure of his fingers on her skin was featherlight, but she knew that if she tried to pull away they would hold her like high-tensile steel.

If she was going to be truly honest she would have to tell him that the only reason she was here was because of Neil. Neil and his mistress, and his ruthless ambition, she thought with sudden bleakness. But she had absolutely no intention of sharing her private problems with Mr Ewan Cameron.

She bit her lip and then looked up at him. 'I've simply come to discuss the bequest,' she said as firmly as she could.

'Uh-huh.' The look in those blue eyes of his was nothing if not disbelieving. 'You're running away from something, aren't you?' said Ewan. 'Or perhaps I should say some*one*. Like this so-called fiancé of yours.'

'It's none of your business!' she burst out, needled by his intent stare.

'You made it my business as soon as you knocked on my door tonight,' he replied.

'You did read that letter, didn't you?' she demanded fiercely. 'Or can't you read?' She stopped suddenly, appalled at what she had said.

His eyes held hers and she looked away first. 'I'm sorry,' she muttered, passing a weary hand over her forehead. 'I shouldn't have said that.'

'I guess not,' he agreed slowly, his eyes regarding her coldly. 'But I didn't ask for you to come here, and now you're here I don't think much of your manners.'

'*My* manners?' retorted Caron. 'That's pretty rich, coming from you.'

Ewan grinned suddenly. 'I thought women like you were supposed to like the down-home approach from simple cowboys like me,' he said smoothly.

'You're about as simple as Einstein's theory of relativity,' said Caron caustically.

'Is that Bill Einstein in Wyoming, or his distant relatives in Montana?' mocked Ewan.

Caron opened her mouth and then closed it again.

Ewan looked at her consideringly. 'What do you know about me?' he said softly.

Caron's glance flickered around the comfortable, cosy room and then back to him. 'Not much,' she admitted.

'You didn't have a brief?' he pursued.

She shrugged miserably. 'My father was dealing with it, but he was taken ill. One of the partners gave me a quick idea of what was involved, but I was going to read all the documents on the plane. Then I realised I'd put the papers in my suitcase, which by that time was in the hold.

'All I had was the copy of my letter, and what Mr Benton told me, although it all seems a bit of a haze now. It was my father who was going to come out here originally, you see.' She shrugged. 'In the circumstances I didn't think it really mattered.'

'Some lawyer,' grunted Ewan.

'I thought you were a frail old man,' Caron burst out. 'The same age as your cousin. I thought you were going to be so glad about the money. I didn't expect—'

'The Spanish Inquisition?' enquired Ewan with a glint in his eye.

She rubbed her forehead distractedly. 'I'm sorry,' she muttered. 'I haven't been thinking straight lately. I've fallen down on the job and there's no excuse. But after I've read all the papers tomorrow I can brief you fully.'

They stared at each other for a long moment. 'Maybe I've been a little hard on you,' said Ewan.

She had expected a searing attack on her efficiency, not an apology. She had been geared up to fight back, and his gentleness almost fazed her completely.

'Maybe a little hard,' agreed Caron noncommittally.

'There's a phone over there,' he said, gesturing to it. 'You can ring your fiancé if you like.'

'No!' she objected fiercely. 'I don't want to.'

She swallowed hard, trying to regain her calmness. 'I mean,' she faltered, 'it's not necessary.'

He gazed at her with those eyes that missed absolutely nothing. 'What are you so scared of, Caron?'

'I'm not scared,' she denied, her voice cracking with strain and tiredness.

'Your hands are shaking and your eyes are just about as wide open as they could be. I'd say that was a pretty good indication of fear,' he replied.

She said nothing, knowing that she would not be able to control the quaver in her voice.

'You know,' he continued, 'if I didn't know better I'd say you were definitely a runaway.'

'Don't be ridiculous,' she protested.

Ewan gazed at her, and then, before she could do anything practical to prevent it, he picked up her handbag.

'What...what are you doing?' she said breathlessly.

'Checking up on you,' replied Ewan. 'You got any objections?'

'Give me my bag back,' she forced out.

He glanced at her wordlessly, put the big leather bag between them, unsnapped the catch, and tipped the contents onto the sofa.

'How dare you?' she said furiously, grabbing a lipstick as it rolled to the edge of a cushion.

He caught her hand and looked at the small metal cylinder. 'Siren's Call, huh?' he said, reading the little label on the end of the tube. 'Not really your colour,' he mused, releasing her wrist.

Caron reddened. 'I'm not responsible for the stupid names they give lipsticks.'

She felt a bolt of pure shock as he reached out and gently traced the outline of her lips with one of his forefingers. 'They're more the colour of soft coral,' he said, and then abruptly dropped his hand.

She stared at him, utterly unmanned by his unexpected gesture. His eyes were back on the contents of her handbag now, as if nothing had happened. It was ridiculous, the way he was affecting her.

'What do you know about make-up?' she snapped suddenly, stuffing the lipstick back into her bag. 'Or do you order the latest shades for your horse?'

He smiled. 'Not a bad idea,' he conceded, his long fingers searching out a battered photograph.

The tension in her body was almost at breaking-point. 'Leave that alone!' she yelled, trying to grab it from him. 'Just who do you think you are?'

Ewan held the picture out of her reach and looked at her. 'You come to a stranger's house in the middle of nowhere at night, and you ask me how I dare do something?' He shook his head. 'I'm a careful man, Caron. When strange people turn up out of the blue on my doorstep I like to know that they are exactly who they say they are.'

'I told you—' began Caron.

'Yes, I know,' said Ewan. 'And I guess I could safely swear that you are indeed who you say you are.' His eyes rested on her angry face. 'Shame you can't be so certain about me, though.'

'You're Ewan Cameron,' she replied weakly.

'You only think that because that's what I told you,' he pointed out. 'I could just have finished murdering the real Ewan Cameron for his inheritance money a few moments before you knocked on the door.'

Caron made another unsuccessful grab for the picture. 'Don't be ridiculous,' she snapped. 'The taxi driver knew who you were.'

Ewan looked seriously at her. 'It's not so ridiculous, Caron. If you think about it, I may not be a murderer or a rapist but you don't know me at all.'

A shaft of real fear suddenly rendered her instantly, tremblingly awake. She remembered the fanciful idea she had squashed down earlier and looked him straight in the face. 'You...you haven't just come out of prison, have you?' she said.

The look of astonishment on his face was genuine and the relief made her feel weak. Somehow she couldn't bear the idea that he was a criminal.

'No, I haven't just come out of jail,' he said slowly. 'But I'm glad to see you do have some suspicions about complete strangers.'

'Sweet of you,' she retorted.

His eyes narrowed. 'You don't seem to have the sense God gave a box of rocks if you think you can just trust any old stranger you meet when you're thousands of miles from home with just a few dollars in your bag. And you don't know anything about me. I'm just trying to make you see sense, that's all.'

'I know you're a pretty good horseman,' she said in a small voice.

His face softened, and Caron felt a breath catch deep in her throat as he turned his soft midnight gaze on her.

'Billy the Kid and Geronimo were pretty good horsemen,' he remarked, 'but that doesn't mean you'd want to spend a weekend with them.'

Caron was silent. There was nothing she could say, because, in essence, Ewan was perfectly right. She must have been mad to come here, but it had been her only escape route.

Now she didn't know what she'd really been expecting to achieve by her sudden flight. But she certainly hadn't expected this disconcertingly handsome man who talked so quietly and thought so fast.

He looked at the photograph he was still holding. 'This Neil?' he said. Caron nodded numbly. 'Never trust a guy who dyes his hair,' said Ewan.

She snatched the photo from him. 'It's none of your business!' she cried.

He gazed at her sardonically. 'You're a real spitfire when you get going, aren't you?'

Caron clenched her teeth.

'If you think he's so great,' Ewan pursued, 'how come you don't want to call him?'

'I... We've...' Caron stopped.

Ewan raised an eyebrow. 'Lovers' tiff? Pre-wedding strain?'

She wondered whether to tell him the truth, and decided against it. It was too painful to think about what had happened in London, never mind put into words for the benefit of a complete stranger. She shook her head. 'I'd rather not talk about it,' she said as brusquely as she could.

He looked at her slowly. 'You want to make him sweat?'

Caron's mouth opened in surprise and then she nodded. 'Yes,' she lied quickly. 'I don't want him to know where I am.'

There was a look in Ewan's eyes now that she didn't altogether care for. As if he could see inside her and he didn't much like what he saw.

'OK, Caron Lane the solicitor,' he said at last, 'I'll make a deal with you.'

'Deal?' she queried tentatively. 'But I don't need to make any deals with you.'

'Oh, yes, you do,' he contradicted her. 'Otherwise how are you going to make out until Tuesday?'

'You can give me a lift to town,' said Caron. 'If you would be so good, that is,' she added hurriedly, seeing the flash of impatience in his eyes at her peremptory words. 'And I can stay in one of those other hotels you mentioned. I'll just get everything charged up to my account and pay when the banks finally open. I can get some money wired to me by then.'

'Doesn't seem as though I get much out of the arrangement,' replied Ewan thoughtfully. 'Except the belated satisfaction of having taught you some manners.'

'You get an inheritance,' snapped Caron. 'And a fairly sizeable one at that. What more do you want?'

'A housekeeper,' he said simply.

'Well, now you can afford one,' she answered sweetly, not having the slightest suspicion of what he was going to say next.

He nodded, amusement warming his eyes. 'That's true. But I think I prefer the bargain I have in mind. I need a housekeeper now, until the new one shows up next week. This house is a mess and I get tired of my own cooking.'

Caron stood up suddenly, alarmed at his reasoning and the way he was looking at her. 'Now wait just a second,' she said. 'If you're suggesting what I think you are . . .'

'Damn right I am,' said Ewan. 'You can fill in here as a housekeeper until after the bank holiday. No hotel in town is going to take you on trust if you can't show them a credit card. So I'm doing you a big favour.'

'Some favour,' spat Caron.

He looked at her levelly. 'You better believe it, lady. As payment you can have bed and board here and I will take you to Calgary on Tuesday so you can catch your plane. Otherwise you can just give me the papers and go right now.'

Their eyes locked. 'You're the most unreasonable person I've ever met!' Caron burst out.

'Likewise,' said Ewan softly.

'But the wedding's in a week's time and I—'

'I guarantee you won't miss the ceremony,' he interrupted. 'Besides,' he added blandly, 'this will be a great opportunity for you to brush up on all those little housewifely duties which I'm sure good old Neil will appreciate.'

Caron glared at him. 'I am a fully qualified solicitor,' she bit out. 'And I have no intention of wasting my time making beds and doing the dishes for Neil, you or anyone else.'

Ewan stretched out a little more comfortably on the sofa and closed his eyes. 'Door's over there,' he said, motioning to it. 'You will close it behind you, won't you?'

Caron stood like a deer poised for sudden flight and stared angrily at his oh, so relaxed body. 'Damn you, Ewan Cameron, I didn't come all the way out here to do your dishes.'

'No,' he said consideringly. 'You swanned out here to wriggle out of your responsibilities to the man you are supposed to be marrying. And meanwhile good old, relevant old Neil is probably worrying his heart out about where you are.'

'You've got it all wrong,' gasped Caron.

He opened his eyes and gazed steadily at her. 'Have I?' he said softly. 'And maybe Neil has got you all wrong.'

'What do you mean?' Caron forced out.

He looked at her assessingly and then said calmly, 'For a girl who's getting married in a week's time you sure seem anxious to keep your fiancé at arm's length. Is that why you keep a photograph of him?'

'What do you mean?' asked Caron unthinkingly.

'So you can recognise him on your wedding night?'

This was going too far. 'Who on earth do you think I am?' she blazed, taking a step towards him, her fists clenched.

'*What* would be more accurate,' he countered softly, the implied insult only too clear.

Almost without thinking she took another step towards him and lashed out, but Ewan was quicker. He grabbed her wrist and pulled her close. Caron tried to wrench away, but it was useless. 'Stop it,' she gasped, struggling.

'And just what does Miss Lane, the sophisticated English lawyer, intend to do if I don't?' he enquired.

Caron swallowed. 'I'm going to ring the police and get you arrested for sexual harassment,' she said as bravely as she could, realising as she spoke how ridiculous her words sounded.

'Really?' he enquired, his voice casual but his eyes as cold as deep water. 'If it's harassment you're after, I'm sure I can do much better than just hold your hand.'

His nearness and simple animal magnetism were almost more than she could stand. 'No, I—' she began, but she could say no more. Ewan's lips were on hers, his arms pulling her close, his whole body claiming hers in a way Neil's had never done. She didn't want to struggle as his tongue tasted the sweet moisture of her mouth. She wanted him to go on, to—

Suddenly appalled at the way she was responding, she put her hands on his chest and tried to push him away.

Instantly he released her, as if the very touch of her skin burned him.

He looked down at her and said, 'Telephone's over there if you still want to ring the police.'

His face was no more than a few inches away from her own. 'You've got it all wrong about me,' she whispered. 'Really you have.'

'Prove me wrong, then, Caron Lane the solicitor,' he said grimly. 'But I'll bet you a dollar to my best horse that you can't.'

Caron touched her lips with trembling fingers and then, conscious of the way he was staring at her, pulled them away and clasped her hands in her lap.

There was really no way out. She would have to accept Ewan's deal, but it didn't mean she was going to surrender meekly. 'If this is the way you interview all your job applicants,' she said icily, 'I'm not surprised your housekeeper has quit.'

Ewan put a finger under her chin and tilted it up towards him. 'You going to turn the offer down?' he asked.

Caron's eyes sparked. 'I'll stay,' she said shortly.

'Good,' he replied.

Caron opened her eyes in the darkness and reached for the bedside light. It was only five-thirty, but she felt wide awake. It was probably about midday in England and sleep was the last thing on her jet-lagged mind.

A hot drink was what she needed. Throwing back the covers and swinging her legs to the floor, she reached for her thin silk wrap and made for the kitchen.

The light dazzled her momentarily as she switched it on and then, as her eyes focused properly on the room, she gasped at the mess it was in. No wonder Ewan had needed a housekeeper. The place looked as if a bomb had hit it.

Piles of dirty dishes tottered on work surfaces which were sticky with dust and spilt beer and the overflowing contents of several ashtrays. Cold fury coursed through her veins at the idea that she was expected to clean this up. It was just not on.

'I won't do it,' she said out loud. 'I simply won't.'

'You can't back out now,' came a voice she was beginning to know only too well, and she whirled round to find Ewan in the doorway.

'You said housekeeping,' flared Caron, desperately tightening the silk tie of her robe as his eyes lingered over her body. 'Not cleaning the Stygian stables.'

He pushed himself off the doorjamb and walked towards her. 'I think you'll find the stables in question were Augean,' he corrected her gently.

Her mouth opened in surprise but no sound came out. He walked past her to the counter and extracted a coffee-pot from the assembled junk. He began to rinse it out under the tap. His movements seemed slow but he had a grace and economy of movement that Caron found compelling to watch. He half turned to her. 'What's the matter?' he enquired.

She shook herself back to reality like an angry cat.

'Nothing,' she snapped. 'Absolutely nothing.'

'Well,' he smiled, shaking the pot of the last remaining water droplets, 'I guess that's all right, then.'

Caron wanted to stamp her foot. 'It's not bloody all right and you know it!' she blazed. 'If you need a char you should get a proper one, like I do at my flat in London. Then it doesn't matter how much mess you make because there's always someone else to clean it up.'

Ewan spooned coffee into the pot. 'Well, this time,' he drawled, 'that someone else is you.'

'But the place is filthy,' she spat.

'I know,' he replied. 'But I'm sure a woman of your calibre will soon have it all in apple-pie order. It'll be very character-building for you.'

Caron glared at him. 'I don't need my character built, thank you.'

He looked at her speculatively, a small smile playing across his lips. 'Well, then, maybe bits of it could do with some demolition.'

She drummed her fingers on the counter and tried to count to ten, before meeting his eyes again. 'How did it get like this, anyway?' she demanded.

Ewan shrugged. 'It wasn't so difficult. It takes a great deal of work to transport a couple of hundred horses from Calgary out here every spring and the boys used this place in the last few weeks while repairs to their bunkhouse were being carried out.'

'The boys?' echoed Caron. 'What boys? Cowboys?'

He nodded. 'If you like. Some of them prefer to be called wranglers but,' he shrugged, 'it's all one and the same thing.'

'I hope you charged them a decent rent,' said Caron. 'If I were you I'd have complained to their boss and got them to clean it up or offer you compensation. This mess is disgraceful.'

For some reason, Ewan seemed to find her words vastly amusing. 'Well,' he said at last, 'I'm just a poor illiterate cowboy myself. Claiming compensation seems a little out of my range.'

Caron gazed at him narrowly. 'Why do you say you're illiterate?'

'You were the one who seemed to assume for some reason last night that I couldn't read,' he replied calmly.

The memory of their conversation flooded back and Caron flushed at her crassness. 'But that was just a heat of the moment thing,' she protested. 'You know I didn't mean it.'

'Do I?' he challenged. 'Seems you think you can just ride right over everybody, and nobody ever tells you no.'

'That's not true,' denied Caron.

'How about Neil?' Ewan asked softly. 'Does he stand up to you?'

'Neil doesn't need to stand up to me,' she retorted. 'It's me—' She stopped dead as she realised how near she was coming to telling the truth about her fiancé. She flushed under Ewan's shrewd gaze.

'It's me what?' he prompted.

She pressed her lips together angrily. 'This is ridiculous,' she snapped. 'I don't have to tell you anything about my private life. You're just making me sound like some acid-tongued virago, that's all.'

He gazed at her and said nothing.

'I'm not anything of the sort,' she burst out. 'Don't you dare look at me like that, Ewan Cameron. All this stuff is just exaggeration and you know it.'

He shrugged. 'Maybe,' he agreed. 'But you have to admit you came here last night with a whole string of preconceptions about what you were going to find.'

'Yes,' she bit out. 'I suppose I did. I thought you were going to be a decent civilised human being, instead of some backwoods slave-driver who has more dirty crockery than a motorway service station.'

Ewan put his coffee-cup down slowly on the counter and gazed at her steadily. His hand reached out and caressed the back of her neck, pulling her closer. She did not resist.

The touch of his lips on hers was butterfly-light but as unsettling as if she had been given an electric shock.

Then his hand dropped and he smiled into her troubled eyes. 'I'd love to show you some more of my backwoods charm, Caron, but I have work to do.' He looked around the kitchen before adding, 'And so do you.'

Caron stared furiously at him, angry at him for kissing her, angry at herself for letting him. 'If you think, for one second, that I am going to clean up this mess you are completely off your rocker.' She lifted her chin. 'It's still only the middle of the night and I'm going back to bed.'

She turned on her heel and marched back to her bedroom. She could feel his eyes boring into the back of her neck as she crossed the passage. And as she closed the door behind her she suddenly ran to the bed and buried herself under the covers.

Two seconds later the door slammed open as if a western blizzard had just blown through it.

Caron poked her head cautiously out of the blankets. Ewan was standing at the end of her bed, looking at her as if she were a particularly badly schooled horse and he couldn't make up his mind whether to buy her or not.

'Come on,' he said. 'Up.' And, striding to the window, he pulled open the curtains, letting the first weak rays of dawn filter in.

Caron held the sheets up to her nose with shaking hands. 'No,' she muttered indistinctly.

'What did you say?' he enquired.

She lowered the sheet to her chin. 'I said no,' she told him. 'I'm not going to get up. I don't want to and you can't make me.'

She swallowed as he came right up to the bed and stared down at her. 'Oh, can't I?' he said softly.

'I'm a free woman,' she said. 'Don't you dare threaten me.'

Ewan held her gaze. 'A deal is a deal, Caron.'

'I said I'd be your housekeeper,' she flared. 'I didn't think I'd have to practically muck you out.'

His lips twitched. 'Guess you should have taken more of a look round before you agreed to buy a pig in a poke.'

Caron dropped her eyes to the sheet she was holding and muttered, 'Pig in a pigsty, you mean. Well, it's not fair and I won't do it.'

The words dropped into a silence that became positively ominous as she realised how pathetically childish she had sounded. But she would not lift her head to look at him.

Ewan walked out of the room. Caron breathed a sigh of relief, but two minutes later he returned, one of his hands behind his back. 'You going to get up?' he asked.

Caron hoped she looked braver than she felt. 'No,' she snapped. 'What are you going to do about it? Plug me with a six-shooter or something?'

'Not quite,' he sighed. 'But don't say I didn't warn you.' He brought his hand out from behind his back and Caron could see that he was holding a jug.

'What—?' she began, and then gasped as a shining arc of icy water hit her in the face.

'You beast!' she screamed, leaping from the bed, her thin nightdress sticking clammily to her. 'You rotten, rotten beast!'

Ewan smiled at her, the jug dangling from his hand. 'So I'm a beast now, as well as all those other things. Guess I've sure learned a lot about myself in the last few hours.'

He set the jug down on a chest of drawers. 'I'd get dressed if I were you,' he drawled. 'You'll catch your death of cold otherwise.'

'Why not just let me?' chattered Caron. 'That would solve all our problems.'

He stood stock-still then, looking at her as if he had never really seen her before. 'You really don't care about anything, do you?' he said softly.

'I care about my clients,' she muttered.

'But not about Neil?' he probed. She was silent. 'And you certainly don't seem to think too much about yourself,' he mused. 'I guess you really would sit there all day waiting to catch a chill.'

She stared at him fiercely. 'What's it to you what happens to me?' she demanded.

He ripped the counterpane from her bed and wrapped it round her, pushing her down onto the mattress. 'You're my new housekeeper, remember?' he said. 'Can't have you keeling over before you've even scrubbed one floor.'

'Throwing that water over me was a really low trick,' forced out Caron as he sat down next to her and began rubbing her hands.

'Yes,' agreed Ewan, 'I guess it was. But I reckon you deserved it.'

She pulled the blanket more tightly around her body, all too aware of how the saturated nightdress was outlining every curve in her body.

'Deserved it?' she repeated, shivering uncontrollably. She could feel the warmth of his body and resisted the urge to move closer to him. 'Me? You're the one who should have a jug of cold water thrown over you.'

CHAPTER THREE

EWAN'S hands closed suddenly around her wrists, pulling her to him. 'You know, you're the strangest woman I've ever met,' he said. 'You've got a look in your eyes that's almost desperate and yet here you are ready to spit at the devil himself. What's your secret, Caron?'

His body was warm against hers and so comforting. She closed her eyes against the tidal wave of despair that was threatening to overwhelm her.

She had so little time to solve her problems, but every possible avenue of escape was firmly marked 'No Exit'. Unless some sort of miracle occurred in the next week, she would have to give herself on Saturday to a man who was blackmailing her.

Ewan's arms closed about her and the breath caught in her throat. There was a simple, very human need in her to respond, to ask for an affection and understanding that she had not had for a long, long time— that she had almost forgotten that she needed. But with a mental shake she schooled herself to be still, neither giving nor accepting the warmth that she wanted so badly.

Then his arms dropped and the warmth was gone. The weight on the mattress shifted and she opened her eyes to see him standing by the bed, looking at her as if he had never seen her before. Their gaze locked and she waited for him to say something caustic. It would take only one word to shatter her overstretched defences.

41

A finger trailed down her cheek and she shivered at his touch. He smiled right down into her eyes. 'I guess I can't physically make you keep your part of the deal, Caron,' he said gently. 'I've never liked bullies and I don't intend to turn into one just to get my house clean.'

She opened her mouth but he continued, 'It's going to be a beautiful day. Seems a shame to waste it by going back to bed.' And before she could reply he had turned and walked out of the room.

Caron had to admit that the kitchen, after she had spent nearly three hours cleaning it, was really very pretty. Unlike her, she thought wryly. How had she got so dirty, when all she had done was clean things? Her nail varnish was chipped and her fingernails were positively black. No wonder the housekeeper at home was always buying rubber gloves.

She sighed at the thought of Mrs Peabody. If only she could have called her in now. She would have had the whole house shining, practically in the time it took Caron to have a bath.

But all Caron had managed was the kitchen and she had a sinking feeling that Ewan was going to be back any moment. She lifted her chin. Well, she had done her best, and he was just going to have to be happy with that.

She made herself a cup of coffee and leant against the counter to admire her handiwork. It was really rather impressive, if you didn't examine anything too closely.

The pine table and chair and the wood-panelled walls shone, even if they were a bit sticky with polish. The glass-fronted cupboards might be slightly streaked but they were clean. It all combined to look—almost—like some feature on country kitchens in a glossy magazine.

Her eyes fell on the two large plastic sacks she had filled with rubbish and she sighed. They really had to go outside, and she supposed she was going to have to be the one to take them.

Putting her mug down, she opened the screen door, grasped the bags and then pushed down the handle of the back door with her elbow.

She had left all the blinds down in the kitchen while she cleaned, feeling somehow that outside the house the scenery would be wild and dark and forbidding, like the blurred impression she retained of the scenery on last night's drive.

But as she turned to face the full majesty of her surroundings in the morning sunshine the bags slithered out of her hands and she walked unheeding to the veranda rail. She had quite simply never seen anything like the scenery that was now all around her.

The back door was on the side of the house and the view it commanded was of a sun-washed meadow in a bowl of snow-capped mountains. The air was fresh with the faint smell of pine.

Numbly she sat on the porch step and took in the view. There was a big barn down below her and some smaller buildings. There were white-railed paddocks and some horses were grazing peacefully.

She could see the road go past the barn and there were cars and quite a few people who certainly didn't look like cowboys. Then she noticed a man riding a horse— a big bay—and leading another one. He was heading in her direction.

Caron stood up suddenly, smoothing her hands nervously on the back of her leggings. The man was wearing a cowboy hat and his face was in shadow but she knew it was Ewan. Knew by the relaxed way he sat the horse and controlled the other one, while making it look like the easiest thing in the world.

She felt an almost overwhelming urge to run back into the house; to hide somewhere—anywhere—from this infuriating, fascinating man. But she stood her ground and forced herself to look calm as he slid off his horse and looped the reins easily over the veranda rail. What had she got to be nervous about?

She folded her arms as if her body language would ward him off, and her tone was challenging. 'Come for a tour of inspection?' she said.

Ewan whacked his hat against his jeans and walked up the porch steps. 'No,' he replied.

She pursed her lips. 'I've been slaving all morning over your blasted house. You might at least want to see it.'

He bit back a smile. 'You aiming for a good-conduct medal?'

Caron flushed. 'Certainly not.' Then she added primly, 'I've just been keeping my part of the bargain, that's all.'

He nodded slowly, taking in her tired eyes and dirt-streaked hands and face. 'Thought you might like to come for a ride,' he offered.

Her heart leapt at the idea. 'Oh, yes!' she said with a childish enthusiasm that made him smile. Then her face clouded. 'Can you get the time off?' she said uncertainly.

'Oh, I can get all the time off I need,' he replied expressionlessly. 'My boss understands me completely.'

Caron frowned. 'You shouldn't get too arrogant on account of this inheritance,' she urged impulsively. 'It might take a while for the money to come through and you don't want to alienate people.'

For some reason he seemed to find this very funny. Her eyes narrowed. 'I give you good advice and you just stand there and laugh,' she said stiffly.

He looked at her for a moment, the smile still on his face. Then, dropping the stetson on the floor, he walked up to her and gathered her into his arms. 'Just what do you think you are doing?' she demanded unsteadily, her pulse seeming to thunder in her ears.

'I'm going to kiss you,' he said simply. 'After all, as you said, it wouldn't do to alienate people, especially a solicitor who's a long way from home.'

He smelt of soap and raw masculine energy and before she could think of any reasoned argument for not responding to him his lips were on hers and her fingers reached up to twine in the hair at the back of his neck, her body responding to his with a hunger she had never known before.

Her eyes fluttered open to see him staring down at her, as if gauging her response. And suddenly she pulled away. She backed up to the veranda rail, unable to take her eyes off him. 'I can't do this,' she said hoarsely. 'I only met you last night and I—'

He lifted his hands. 'I know,' he said softly. 'You're getting married on Saturday to a man you're keeping on a string.'

'It's not like that at all,' she muttered.

'Explain it to me, then,' he demanded.

Caron swallowed. 'Wouldn't you rather have breakfast?' she said abruptly. 'I expect you're hungry after working all this time.' She pushed herself off the rail and sidled round Ewan to enter the house. 'I'm really quite a good cook,' she rattled on nervously. 'My bacon and eggs could win prizes.'

'Just as well there aren't any competitions for liars,' he mused, following her into the house.

Caron, already at the stove, froze at his words. Then she whirled around to face him, a frying-pan in her hand. 'And just what is that supposed to mean?' she demanded.

Ewan hooked a thumb through one his belt loops and smiled down at her. 'You gonna hit me with that or put it on the stove?'

'Hitting you wouldn't achieve anything,' she bit out.

He studied her flushed face. 'Glad to see you learnt something last night,' he said.

Caron glared at him, remembering only too well how she had flown at him the previous evening. 'Why should I go to the effort of attacking you,' she said as bravely as she could, 'when you obviously have no feelings at all? You probably wouldn't feel anything if an entire frying-pan factory fell on your head.'

'Just the same,' said Ewan calmly, taking the pan from her and putting it on the stove, 'I'd feel happier if this had eggs in it, instead of my head.'

'You must have some sort of persecution complex,' she said lightly, desperately trying to break the tension that was beginning to build up around them. Ewan stared at her without comment, and Caron turned hurriedly back to the stove. Why, in the middle of trying to insult him, did she have to think suddenly that his eyes were the most beautiful colour she had ever seen?

When he spoke his voice was relaxed, easy, as if they had been exchanging pleasantries. 'No,' he replied. 'No complex. Just a highly developed instinct for survival. Especially when I've just called someone a liar.'

'I'm not a liar,' she flared. 'And you have no reason to call me one.'

'OK,' he agreed. 'Maybe "liar" wasn't exactly the right word. But you're definitely hiding something, Caron. I've met girls before who were just plain nervy, but you're so highly strung I could play a tune on you.'

Caron took an egg from the rack and crashed it into the pan. 'Scrambled eggs be all right?' she said suddenly, staring at the mixed-up mess in front of her.

He pushed her gently out of the way. 'Here, I'll cook breakfast.'

Caron glared at him. 'Isn't this what you employed me for?' she said caustically.

His eyes softened with humour. 'Guess I did,' he agreed. 'But the way you were going I'd still be waiting for my breakfast next Christmas.'

'I'm perfectly capable of knocking up bacon and eggs,' snarled Caron.

'Maybe,' Ewan conceded, his face unreadable. 'But the whole point about electric stoves is that you have to switch them on before they start to work. They're funny like that.'

Caron's lips parted, but she could find nothing to say. How could she have been so foolish?

Ewan looked sympathetically at her. 'Go on, sit down. You look practically all in.'

'I'm sorry,' she muttered.

'No need,' he replied, equably, his fingers reaching out to cup her jaw, his thumb caressing her cheek.

Caron could feel tears pricking her eyelids and she swallowed hard. She could not, would not break down in front of this man.

She had trusted Neil and he had betrayed her. She hadn't even known Ewan Cameron for twenty-four hours. That wasn't long enough to trust anyone.

Besides, she thought bitterly, she didn't think she would be able to trust anyone ever again, not after what Neil had done, not even if she knew them for a lifetime. She pulled Ewan's hand from her face with an effort and turned blindly away.

'I'm sorry,' she choked out again. 'I think I have a cold coming on. I'll just go and get some tissues.'

He looked at her assessingly and then caught her arm. 'It's no good, Caron,' he said. 'I always find out the truth in the end.'

She stared up at him. 'We might as well be complete strangers,' she snapped. 'How could you find out anything about me?'

He shrugged. 'You could say it's a speciality of mine—finding out how people tick. Especially when their eyes are my favourite colour.'

'The way I tick is absolutely none of your business,' she retorted, wrenching her arm away and making a grab for the door.

But he was too quick for her. His hand closed over hers and he turned her to face him. 'Look at me, Caron,' he said softly, and then, as she did not lift her face, he tipped her chin up. Unable to keep up her façade any longer, she felt tears begin to well in her eyes.

Ewan's arms slid round her and she buried her head in his shoulder and burst into tears. He held her silently and as her sobs died he passed her his handkerchief.

'Look,' he sighed, 'why don't you call the guy? If he's got any sense at all he'll forgive you for what you've done.'

Caron pulled back in Ewan's arms and looked up at him. 'Forgive me?' she said fiercely. 'That's just typical of a man, isn't it?'

Ewan's face hardened. 'Well, you're the one who's run out on him. You're the one who won't even call him to put his mind at rest.'

Caron shook herself free and made for the door. 'You don't know anything about me, Ewan Cameron. All you seem to know about is horses. So that hardly qualifies you to tell me how to run my life.'

He glared at her, but his voice was silky smooth. 'In that case,' he drawled, 'maybe I should have been a dog breeder.'

He sidestepped easily as she ran at him, more furious than she had ever been in her life. Catching her around the waist, he booted open the back door and carried her kicking and screaming down the steps to a horse trough. 'I only had time to give you a quick shower this morning,' he said. 'Maybe now it's time for you to have a full tub.'

'You wouldn't dare!' she screamed, looking in horror at the dark water.

'Want to bet?' he replied, before loosening his grip and dumping her in the trough.

Gasping and choking, she stood up to tell Ewan exactly what she thought of him. But as she tried to scramble to her feet she slid on the slimy bottom of the trough and fell back in.

'Don't you dare laugh at me!' she yelled, choking on the icy water that splashed through her mouth and nose.

Ewan pressed his lips together and turned his back on her. She could see his shoulders shaking and she swept the hair out of her eyes with an angry hand. 'I don't know why you think I'm so funny,' she ground out, struggling to get upright again.

He turned back to her, his face perfectly straight but with a light in his eyes that made her heart flop unreasonably. 'Well, you see,' he said gently, 'I'm just a hick after all, and we provincial types do have to make our own entertainment.'

She glared at him. 'I'm a solicitor,' she snarled. 'I'm not your entertainment.'

'No?' he said, his words loaded with sarcasm. 'A solicitor? The way you've been acting since you got here I thought you were a card-carrying, twenty-four-carat, spoilt rotten, poor little rich girl.'

Caron clambered carefully out of the trough and stood in front of him. She brushed the excess water from her face with the back of her hand and saw that it came away streaked with mascara. She must look like a complete clown, she thought with a sudden pang, and then, pulling herself together, looked him right in the eye.

'I may come from a wealthy family,' she conceded, 'and if they have spoiled me that's hardly my fault. But I came here with a job to do and precious little thanks I've got for it. My private life is none of your business.'

'No?' he said softly. 'Well, I think it is. I want you, Caron. Don't ask me why, because it's a question I've been asking myself all morning and I still don't know the answer. But since you walked into my house last night everything to do with you is my business.'

Caron swallowed hard. 'That's just animal magnetism or some sort of silly sexual chemistry,' she said quickly.

His eyes lingered on her face. 'So I wasn't wrong,' he said at last. 'We both feel the same way.'

'We do not!' she choked out. 'I don't feel anything for you, Ewan Cameron. I'm getting married in six days' time and this is all...'

'Ridiculous?' supplied Ewan, with a glint in his eye. 'Silly, illogical, nonsensical?'

'More than I can handle,' snapped Caron. 'Every-body's supposed to be awash with emotions before they get married, and you're just taking advantage of mine.'

'Not everybody hightails it to the Rockies to get six thousand miles from their intended husband less than a week before their wedding,' observed Ewan.

Caron wrung half a pint of water from her shirt tail and glared at him. 'I keep telling you, it's my business.'

'I wish I could believe that,' replied Ewan drily. 'Especially the way you resist me when I make a pass at you.'

Caron coloured right up to the roots of her hair. 'If you had any sense of decency you wouldn't make passes at me.'

He smiled at her. 'If you had one you wouldn't react.'

'I told you,' she said as forcefully as she could, 'you just take advantage.'

There was a certain way his eyes twinkled when he looked at her, blast him, she suddenly noticed. She leant back over the trough, her hand groping through the water, acutely aware of how he was looking at her.

'If you were at all a gentleman,' she snapped, 'you'd help me look for my shoes.'

'Who said I was a gentleman?' replied Ewan as he squatted down beside her, his fingers brushing against hers in the murky water. 'No,' he added. 'You might as well know I had my sense of decency removed at birth. Makes life so much simpler, don't you think?'

'I wouldn't know,' retorted Caron. 'But we made a deal, that's all, and I've kept my side of it.'

Ewan nodded slowly. 'Yes, I guess you have. If the rest of the house looks as good as the kitchen I won't feel so bad about taking you on.'

Caron's jaw dropped at the sheer breathtaking arrogance of the man. 'Taking me on?' she repeated incredulously. 'That's rich, coming from you. You practically had to blackmail me to stay.'

'I was doing you a favour,' he corrected her. 'You could have stayed in the woods for all I cared.'

She stood up suddenly. 'Well, maybe I'll do just that,' she retorted.

Ewan got to his feet and stared down at her. 'Guess you would, too.'

Caron tilted her chin defiantly. 'You better believe it. And I bet the woods will be a damn sight cleaner than your house. It took me the whole morning to clean just one room—what with all those disgusting piles of dirty crockery. You should get a dishwasher.'

'Caron,' he said gently. There was a glint in his eyes which she couldn't interpret at all.

'Yes?' she replied uncertainly. ,

'I have got a dishwasher. It's under the draining-board and it looks like a cupboard.'

Her mouth fell open at the realisation of all those useless hours she had spent scrubbing pots and pans. 'You—' she began, but Ewan was quicker.

Grabbing her hand, he began to pull her along to the house. 'I'd love to hear a selection of your latest insults,' he said, 'but if you don't get dried off soon you'll probably catch pneumonia.'

Caron pushed back the mass of her wet hair, now a dark red-gold colour. 'Sweet of you to care,' she snapped, trying without success to wrench her hand away, 'but I can look after myself. I have a very responsible job, you know. I'm perfectly capable of running my own life.'

Ewan stopped and gazed sardonically at her. 'Well, excuse me, ma'am, but right now I figure you probably couldn't even run a hot shower. Come on, hurry up.'

Their eyes locked, and her gaze was the first to drop. Biting her lip in frustration at this infuriating man, she gave in to the insistent pressure on her arm and jogged back breathlessly to the house.

Ewan yanked open the kitchen door, but Caron hung back in sudden dismay. 'Will you stop fighting me?' he said impatiently. 'I am trying to do something *for* you, not *to* you.'

'The front door,' she forced out through chattering teeth.

He stared at her in amazement. 'What?' he said incredulously.

'I don't want to go in through there,' she insisted. 'I want to go in through the front door.'

'Don't be ridiculous,' he said in astonishment. 'What is this? Suddenly remembered you're too good to walk around a kitchen?'

She pulled away from him and stamped her foot on the veranda. 'Don't patronise me,' she snapped. 'And I'm not being ridiculous.'

His eyebrows lifted. 'Guess I've seen everything now,' he said. 'An icy English solicitor having a temper tantrum. You going to stand in the corner and sulk next?'

'I am not having a temper tantrum!' screamed Caron. 'It's a perfectly reasonable request.'

Ewan gazed at her mockingly. 'Yes, well,' he drawled, 'I guess Vlad the Impaler thought he was a perfectly reasonable, down-home kinda guy.'

Caron thought she was going to burst with pent-up fury and frustration. 'You're the one who's being unreasonable,' she forced out. 'It's my floor and I don't want to walk on it.'

Ewan stared at her and then nodded soothingly. 'Yes, of course it's your floor. And after all why should you walk on it? I mean, let's hear it for floors. They've been underfoot for too long. They have rights too, don't they?'

A dimple was showing in his right cheek now and Caron resisted the urge to sock him right in it. She opened her mouth to explain, but he carried right on. 'Tell me,' he said, doing a good impression of a TV interviewer, 'when did this obsession with floors begin? Is it just wooden ones that affect you this way? And, if so, what would you say is the central plank of your beliefs?'

He held an imaginary microphone up to her face, his eyes laughing down at her. Caron breathed in deeply and for the second time that day attempted to count to ten. She got as far as four.

'Ewan Cameron, will you stop treating me as if I have gone completely off my rocker?' she said as calmly as she could.

He spread his hands wide. 'Hey! Did I say anything to give you that impression?'

She glared at him. 'It's a perfectly simple, reasonable request,' she began, 'if only you would just let me explain.' Before he could say anything she plunged hurriedly on. 'It's just that I did not spend half the morning scrubbing your kitchen floor to the point where I could see my face in it just so that we could trail muddy great boot prints all over it again, that's all.'

She bit her lip as the silence stretched between them, and she realised that this time she had gone completely over the top. What on earth must he think of her behaviour? A sudden picture of her spending the night in the woods flashed across her brain. He wouldn't be so unforgiving. Would he?

Caron raised her eyes to his and saw a sudden warmth in them that she had not expected. He grinned down at her and, surprised, she was hard put to it not to smile back.

'Well,' he said softly. 'So much for your "I'm too good to clean your house" speech.'

'I merely take a pride in my work,' she said primly.

'So I see,' he drawled. 'But I'm going to have a big problem living here if I can't walk around on the floors. It's kind of essential, you know.'

'It's not forever,' said Caron hurriedly. 'It's just—'

He looked at her questioningly. She swallowed then added stiffly, 'I know you probably think I'm being very silly but I'm really proud of that floor. And I'd like to be able to admire it for a bit longer before we make it all dirty again. That's all.'

'That's all, huh?' he repeated softly.

She nodded wordlessly and then gazed at him uncomprehendingly as he put his hand on the doorjamb and shucked off his boots. Even without them he still towered over her by a good six inches. 'Come on, then, Caron. Never let it be said that I can't show good manners to a clean floor.'

He moved right up to her and she tried to step back but the wall was behind her. 'What are you doing now?' she quavered.

'Making a compromise,' he said softly. 'It's what lawyers do best, isn't it?'

She attempted a coolness she didn't feel. 'Maybe, but we don't like being compromised, Mr Cameron.'

'Shame,' he murmured, his lips only inches from her own. He was going to kiss her again, she knew it. And there was absolutely nothing she was going to be able to do about it. Nothing, a little ignored voice inside her was saying, that she really wanted to do about it. Her pulse was rocketing out of control and in sudden panic she closed her eyes. And then, it seemed, the world turned upside down.

He had lifted her into his arms and shouldered open the door.

'Put me down!' she said, struggling. 'Just what exactly do you think you are doing?'

His eyes smiled down into hers. 'Making sure we don't muddy the floor.'

'You're so considerate,' she managed, trying hard to sound cool and in control. Which was difficult, she reflected, when she was being held so very securely in his arms.

'Consideration is my middle name,' he replied equably, his feet making no sound as he padded across the boards.

She fought down all the feelings that his nearness was provoking. 'You're going to have to buy a doormat,' she said as calmly as she could. 'Plus more—'

The rest of her words were lost as she and Ewan suddenly seemed to glide towards the far door. 'What the hell...?' he exclaimed.

Caron had enough time to realise that they were falling before they were in a heap on the floor. She opened her eyes to find herself on top of him, his arms still tightly around her.

'My God,' she breathed, a sudden shaft of fear spearing through her at the sight of his closed eyes. 'Ewan?' she faltered.

His eyes flicked open and relief rushed through her. 'What on earth were you playing at?' she demanded

crossly as she realised how worried she had felt at the
sight of his still form.

He stared at her coolly. 'Guess I wanted to examine
your floor a little more closely. Make sure you hadn't
missed anything.'

'You could have broken something,' she accused.
'Been seriously hurt.'

'You don't say,' he murmured.

She stared at him. 'Ewan?' she repeated. 'Don't you
think we should get up?'

He cocked a look at her, his arms tightening around
her. 'Oh, I don't know,' he drawled. 'I could get to like
this. I might just join your floor-appreciation society.'

She resisted the urge to reach out and touch his face.
'Ewan, I—' she began.

But he was too quick for her. 'Your fiancé's a very
lucky guy,' he said softly.

She stiffened at the mention of Neil. 'You didn't seem
to think that last night,' she snapped.

He stared at her. 'You have a style and a spirit I like,'
he said simply.

Caron dragged her eyes away from his. 'Sounds like
the description of a horse,' she muttered.

He laughed. 'I haven't seen a horse yet that can snap
its eyes and tell me exactly what it thinks of me.'

Once more Caron found herself staring at his face.
She felt as if she was almost drowning in his eyes.

She had vowed to herself not to let any man come
within two feet of her after that row with Neil, and Ewan
was considerably closer than that. She lay tight against
him, her head on his shoulder, her arms around his neck.
'Are you sure you're all right?' she faltered suddenly,
looking up.

He looked at her lazily. 'Well,' he said after a while, 'I'm lying here with another man's woman in my arms. What could be more delightful?'

She sat up suddenly. 'That's a horrible thing to say.'

'Maybe,' he said guardedly. 'But it happens to be true.'

She stared at him. 'I don't belong to anybody. I'm not a thing to be possessed like a . . .' she paused '. . . like a parcel. I'm me. My own woman.'

Ewan suddenly looked tired. 'That sounds all very fine and noble, Caron, except that is all it is: sounds. If you were truly your own woman you wouldn't be planning on making promises you obviously don't want to keep to someone who is supposed to be the biggest thing in your life.'

Caron opened her mouth and then closed it again. 'It's none of your business,' she said sharply. Too sharply. 'Why don't you just leave me alone?'

His fingers brushed her cheek and she trembled involuntarily. 'Maybe I don't want to,' he drawled. 'And maybe I figure you don't want me to either.'

She scrambled to her feet, blushing scarlet. 'That's outrageous,' she accused.

He sat up, rubbing the back of his head. 'Is it?' he said coolly. 'From where I was lying I could have sworn it was the absolute truth.'

He got to his feet in one fluid movement and gazed down at her. Caron smoothed her hands down her leggings. It was a nervous gesture, she knew, but she just couldn't help it. If only he weren't quite so tall.

She drew herself up to her full height of five feet five. 'I'm going to have a shower,' she said in a rush at last—anything to escape from the tension that was building up inside her, and the uncomfortable way he was looking right into her eyes and down into the darkest corners of her soul, where no one, but no one, was allowed to go.

He shrugged. 'Fine.'

She opened her mouth as a sudden need to explain her predicament overwhelmed her, and then closed it again. What was the point? 'Are you really all right?' she said. 'No broken bones or anything?' she added lightly.

'Hurt my hand, but I guess it's OK,' he said at last. 'I can't think what I slipped on.'

'It must have been the soap,' said Caron as matter-of-factly as she could.

He looked at her questioningly.

'I dropped it on the floor and then I couldn't find it,' she said defensively. 'So I thought I might as well leave it, seeing as it was probably the cleanest thing that's been dropped on the floor in a long, long time.'

Ewan gazed at her for a long moment. 'I know there is logic in that statement,' he said at last, sucking on his grazed hand. 'I just can't figure it out, somehow.'

'That's because you don't have my incisive legal mind,' replied Caron primly, heading for the bathroom.

CHAPTER FOUR

EWAN tapped on the door just as Caron switched off the shower, and, hastily wrapping a towel around herself, she unthinkingly pulled the door wide open.

They stared at each other in silence for several seconds. Ewan's eyes held hers but she was shatteringly aware of the way he was tracing the outline of her body, knew that he was imprinting it on his mind in the same way as she was doing with his.

It would have been so easy to give in to this primeval impulse, to reach out her arms, to let the towel fall and step towards him. So easy and so impossible.

She sighed and the spell was broken. 'You've been in there so long I thought you might be drowning,' he said.

'I was reading a book,' she replied unthinkingly.

'In the shower?' he questioned.

Caron looked blankly at him and then snapped back to reality. 'I'm sorry, what did I say?'

Those deep blue eyes studied her for a long moment. 'Guess you must have been thinking about Neil again,' he remarked, a glint in his eye.

'Who?' she queried, confused, and then, as his eyebrows lifted, added hurriedly, 'Oh, Neil. Yes, of course I was thinking about him. Sorry.'

'You don't need to apologise to me for thinking about the man you're going to marry,' replied Ewan coolly. 'He's the one you should be apologising to.'

'Now just you wait a moment...' began Caron.

But Ewan was too quick for her. 'No, not even half a moment,' he said. He shoved a pair of jeans into her arms. 'They're my sister's,' he said. 'I guess they'll fit you. But be ready in five minutes, OK? If not, I'll go without you.'

He turned on his heel and Caron stood watching his back for a few moments before she stepped back and slammed the door. Leaning against it, she brushed a trembling hand over her forehead. What on earth was the matter with her?

Her system was probably on emotional overload because of the corner Neil had pushed her into, came her glib, common-sense reply. Anybody would be wildly over-reacting to things if they were in the situation she was.

She had to get a grip, that was all. She rubbed her forehead and closed her eyes. The way Ewan had looked at her had meant nothing; the way he had kissed her had meant nothing. And the way she felt when she was with him was just imagination. Just that and nothing more.

She opened her eyes and scowled at herself in the bathroom mirror. She couldn't let herself be affected this way. It was just stupid. Stupid and impossible. Almost, a small voice deep within her said, as stupid and impossible as having to marry Neil on Saturday.

The horses picked their way side by side along the trail through the forest and Caron sighed at the beauty of it all. Ewan shot her a glance. 'Happy?' he said tersely.

She nodded and smiled quickly at him and then looked away. It wasn't true. She wasn't particularly happy, but the silence and beauty of their surroundings had brought her some peace at least.

Ewan had hardly spoken to her since they had begun their ride, and she knew it was because he thought so little of her for running out on Neil. But she had been grateful for the silence.

She tried to let her mind go blank. She didn't want to think about Neil and she certainly didn't want to think about her feelings for Ewan. It was all too complicated. And it was enough, really, just to be riding with him through the sort of scenery she had never really imagined existed.

'You know,' he said at last, his tone softening, 'for a city girl you sure are quiet.'

'I don't like talking when I don't have to,' she said. 'You end up saying things you don't really mean.'

'Cities are full of people like that,' replied Ewan. 'So why do you live there?'

She shrugged. 'I don't really know,' she said. 'I've never really thought about it before. Escape has always seemed like something other people do.'

'Until now,' he commented.

She reached down and smoothed the rough brown hairs of her mare's coat. 'I love the smell of horses, don't you?' she said suddenly. 'There's nothing like it in the world. I had a pony when I was small, and then when I was sent away to school it was sold.'

She looked at Ewan. 'Nobody told me,' she explained. 'He was there when I went, but when I came back he was gone. My father said I had outgrown him, and they hadn't told me anything because they didn't want to upset me.'

Caron fished out the hankie Ewan had given her earlier and blew hard into it. 'So silly,' she said. 'I haven't thought about Pepper for years and now here I am bursting into tears for the second time in one day.'

'You're not crying for your lost pony,' said Ewan harshly. 'You're upset because you thought you could run away from a situation you didn't like, and instead you've carried it all the way here with you.'

'Well, that's my problem, isn't it?' she replied hotly.

She could see a muscle jumping in his cheek. 'I've not really run out on my responsibilities,' she said quietly, suddenly realising that she did not want this man to think badly of her. 'I'll go back to England and face the music, but I just need this time. Time to sort myself out.'

He stared ahead and then glanced at her. 'You need time, but I reckon your fiancé needs another woman.'

Her lips tightened. 'Maybe he does,' she said shortly. And then, digging her heels in and shortening her reins, she put the surprised mare into a canter.

Caron bent low over the horse's neck, urging her to go ever faster, as if she could ride right off the edge of the world with her problems.

The wind in her face was more exhilarating than anything she had known in years. Her hair shook free from its pins and tumbled over her shoulders, whipping across her face, but she didn't care. She wanted to yell with a kind of fierce joy. She was free. Free...

Suddenly, the horse came to a skittering stop and Caron, taken completely by surprise, went straight over the mare's head and landed in a heap on the ground.

She sat up dizzily, conscious that the mare had now galloped off, and, as she looked up, focused on a black bear sitting not fifteen feet away from her. It looked, if anything, as shocked as she felt, but her whole body stilled as she took in its deep fur coat, its shiny black eyes and its long, long claws.

Hoofbeats sounded behind her and then, almost instantaneously, it seemed, Ewan was kneeling at her side, one hand still holding the bay's bridle. 'Can you move?' he said urgently.

She nodded speechlessly, getting to her feet as he supported her with his right arm. 'Get on the horse,' he ordered.

'But the bear...' she said breathlessly, her heart hammering as she saw the great beast lumber to its feet.

'Never mind about the damn bear,' he grated. 'Get on the horse, fast.'

She took one look at his grim face and put a foot in the stirrup, heaving herself up in a way that would not have been approved of by her old pony club. She gathered the reins, unable to take her eyes off the bear or Ewan, who was standing at the horse's head.

'It's coming closer,' she breathed.

'Easy,' he said softly. 'Easy.'

She gulped and he flashed her a comforting glance. 'What are we going to do?' she whispered.

'Nothing,' he said quietly. 'For the moment.'

'Nothing?' she almost squeaked. 'But it could kill us!'

He glanced at her again and this time he was smiling, for goodness' sake. 'I think two people and a horse would be an ambitious dinner, even for a bear,' he drawled. 'In any case, bears don't like horses.'

Caron pushed the hair off her face and looked at him. He was standing there gazing at a bear that seemed at least twice as big as he was, as if he had all the time in the world.

'You OK?' he asked, not turning round again.

'Fine,' Caron managed. 'Just shaken.'

She smoothed trembling hands down the horse's coat and stared at the bear, noting the way the mountain breeze was riffling through its thick, soft fur.

Its big black nose and the shadows round its glittering eyes combined to give it a soulful expression as it stood on the path, looking for all the world like Winnie the Pooh searching for a jar of honey. Its claws, on the other hand, looked as if they could rip through chain-link fencing.

Caron's lips parted as it took one step closer, shaking its head from side to side, seemingly sniffing the air.

'Is it trying to decide whether we'll do for supper?' she quavered.

'No,' replied Ewan softly. 'It's showing us how big and strong it is and warning us not to mess with it.'

'Well, that's fine by me,' she said. 'If you mount up too we can just go home right now and leave it alone.'

She made as if to turn the bay, but Ewan merely tightened his grip on the bridle. 'Just stay where you are,' he said. 'The only thing we're going to do is wait. Apart from anything else we have to find your mare.'

'But I'm sure the bear is coming closer,' Caron hissed. 'Why can't we just make a run for it?'

'It could run as fast as we could, if it wanted,' said Ewan. He shook his head. 'We'll have to try to frighten it off.'

'You're not going to shoot it?' said Caron, horrified.

Ewan looked at her coolly. 'What with?'

Her jaw dropped. 'Don't your sort of people carry guns?'

He shot her a caustic look. 'My sort of people?' he echoed sarcastically.

Caron opened her mouth, closed it again and then coloured right up to her hairline.

'My name is not Wyatt Earp, Caron,' he drawled, smiling slightly at her sheepish expression. 'And this is the late twentieth century. Besides,' he shrugged, 'bears are a protected species.'

Caron looked at the bear, snuffling at the air, and shivered.

'What do you want me to do, then?' she asked shakily as it once more began to move towards them. 'Read him his rights?'

Ewan nodded. 'That's one way of putting it, I guess.' And then, stepping out in front of the horse, he began to clap his hands and yell. 'Come on,' he shouted at Caron. 'You too. Remember you're a lawyer. Make as much noise as you would in court.'

Slowly she stood up in the stirrups and as they yelled the bear gave them one astonished look before dropping on all fours and ambling back into the forest.

Caron sat back in the saddle, feeling weak all over. 'It wouldn't really have killed us, would it?' she asked at last.

'Probably not,' replied Ewan. 'It looked just as surprised as you did, sitting there staring at each other in the middle of the forest. I thought you were interviewing a new client.'

He helped her to dismount, and she struggled to escape from the comfort of his arms. She simply couldn't handle this sort of closeness. 'Well, you don't seem to have broken anything,' he said, releasing her. 'And you didn't land on your head, unfortunately.'

She stared up at his amused features. 'What do you mean "unfortunately"?' she demanded, unable to resist the bait.

He shrugged. 'Well, it might have brought about a complete character change. You know, turned you into a sweet, kind, essentially good-natured woman.'

'You mean a doormat,' she retorted. 'One with "WELCOME" written all over it for some macho caveman type like you.'

He whacked his hat against his legs and put it back on his head, throwing his face immediately into shadow. But he was smiling at her and she knew it, damn him.

'Even cavemen had artistic instincts,' he said smoothly. 'Maybe I should ask you to come up and see my etchings some time.' And, taking hold of the bay's bridle, he set off along the trail in pursuit of the mare.

Caron, infuriated to the point of speechlessness, stood watching him for a moment and then, sure that she could still hear the bear snuffling in the undergrowth, hurried after him.

'I guess the bear just didn't hear us coming,' explained Ewan as they walked along. 'You must have given him a hell of a shock when you burst in on him like that.'

'*Him* a hell of a shock?' snapped Caron, her nerve returning fast. 'I was more than slightly surprised myself.'

He smiled at her. 'I don't see why. This is his home. There are a lot of bears in this forest.'

The mare was standing a little way along the trail, pulling at some grass. Ewan felt carefully down her legs and then looked over his shoulder at Caron. 'No damage done, so that's one bear story with a happy ending.'

'Are there bear stories with unhappy endings?' ventured Caron as they mounted and rode on.

He glanced at her and remarked, 'A tourist came up to these woods one time, had a picnic not too far from here and a bear came right out of the trees to see what was going on.'

'What happened?' breathed Caron.

Ewan shrugged. 'The tourist asked the bear to join him for lunch and they've been exchanging Christmas cards ever since.'

Startled, Caron met his gaze and realised that he was laughing at her. 'Don't make fun of me,' she said tightly.

His lips quirked. 'Why not? You sure look as though you could use some fun in your life.'

There was simply no way of squashing this man, thought Caron angrily. Especially since she knew he was right. 'So what really happened?' she said as coolly as she could.

Ewan smiled. 'You can be so prim, Caron. It's one of the things that really fascinates me about you; makes me wonder what's going on under the surface.'

She gritted her teeth, but before she could even frame a retort he sighed and added, 'Shouldn't really have told you that story, considering what's just happened.'

'Why not?' she asked uncertainly.

'When the grizzly came towards the tourist,' Ewan resumed, 'the tourist threw a doughnut at him. It hit the bear right on the nose by all accounts.'

Caron, still feeling a little trembly, gave a muted squeak of horrified laughter. 'Did the bear go away?' she demanded.

He shook his head. 'No. It mauled the tourist to death.'

Caron swallowed. 'Just as well we didn't have any doughnuts with us,' she forced out.

The silence of the forest seemed to envelop them. Caron rode on, busy with her own thoughts.

'Penny for them,' said Ewan, looking down at her from his tall horse.

She glanced at him and half smiled. 'I'd rather have a doughnut for them,' she replied. 'That story you just told me reminds me that in the end we didn't have anything to eat before we set out. And I'm starving.'

'But you had breakfast?' he said questioningly.

Caron shook her head. 'I forgot,' she replied simply.

Ewan's horse came to a sudden stop and he turned to stare at her in astonishment. 'When did you last eat?' he demanded.

Caron wrinkled her forehead. 'On the plane, I suppose,' she said at last. 'No, it was the coffee-shop, just before I realised I'd been robbed. But I had so many things on my mind...'

'Like your deep love for Neil,' he supplied.

She shot him a furious look. 'As I keep telling you, Ewan, my private life is my business. And I don't see that how often or not I think about Neil is of any interest to you.'

'It is if it makes you stop eating,' he pointed out. 'A housekeeper on hunger strike is no use to me at all.'

Caron's eyes sparked at him. 'I didn't ask to be your blasted housekeeper,' she bit out. 'As far as I'm concerned you can take your job and—'

'Yes?' asked Ewan politely, a mocking light in his eyes.

She thought of the alternatives and swallowed hard. 'You know very well that you have me over a barrel with this silly housekeeping scheme of yours,' she forced out at last. 'It's just rotten of you to provoke me like this.'

He turned to her, his eyes glittering with mischief. 'I believe in keeping an eye on the welfare of my staff,' he said blandly. 'Moral as well as physical,' he added pointedly.

Caron drew in her breath sharply. But he just grinned at her and changed the subject again. 'So exactly how hungry are you?' he probed.

'Starving, if you must know,' she said crossly.

'Must be terrible to be so in love,' he mused, looking straight ahead, 'that you just forget to eat.' He sighed heavily. 'Still, don't worry,' he resumed. 'I'll lay it on real thick how you're pining for him in my cable.'

Caron's jaw dropped. 'What cable?' she managed.

He shot her a sideways glance. 'The one I'm thinking of sending to dear old Neil.'

'You wouldn't dare,' she breathed.

'Why not?' he shrugged. 'You're obviously not going to, and I can hardly let a fellow man worry his heart out over someone like you. I could tell him that you're staying all alone with me and there's absolutely nothing to worry about.'

His tone was mocking but the threat was all too real. Caron licked dry lips. 'You wouldn't dare,' she repeated in a whisper.

'Try me,' he replied. 'Course, I could dress it up a little, just enough to make him jealous—say how you cuddled up to me on the couch last night, how you kissed me this morning. That would sure bring him to heel after your row, wouldn't it?'

'You think I'm a complete bitch, don't you?' said Caron stiffly.

'Did I say that?' he replied blandly.

'You didn't have to,' she retorted. 'You think I'm just using Neil, making him suffer by running out here over some silly argument. Don't you?'

He gazed steadily at her. 'What other explanation is there?'

She met his eyes and her jaw clenched. 'One that I'm not going to tell you,' she forced out.

'Suit yourself,' he shrugged.

'I generally do,' she snapped.

Ewan raised an eyebrow. 'Can't say I hadn't noticed.'

'I'd like to push you right off your horse,' Caron gritted.

He flashed her a glance. 'I wouldn't advise it,' he drawled. 'You've obviously been eating so little you probably couldn't even push a button.'

'We would have had bacon and eggs not so long ago if you hadn't decided to throw me into a horse trough,' she said irritably.

Ewan smiled at her. 'A steak would be kinda nice now, wouldn't it? Baked potato, scrambled eggs, coffee, maybe a couple of slices of melon...'

'Stop torturing me,' she hissed. 'I know for a fact you haven't got any food with you. Unless, of course, you're keeping it under your hat.'

'The only thing I keep under my hat, Caron,' he replied, 'is my head. Other people seem to lose theirs so easily, but I know where mine is when I need to use it.'

She opened her mouth and then shut it again. She could hear voices through the trees and, more importantly, smell the unmistakable smell of a barbecue.

'Food,' she breathed. 'Do you think that whoever is having that barbecue might have some to spare?' she asked tentatively.

'I certainly hope so,' he replied. 'Smells like we're just in time. Come on, now.' And, motioning her to follow him, he broke into a canter down the dappled forest trail.

There was a corral under the trees with a group of horses bunched together at one end. Nearby, in a glade, the thin blue smoke of a barbecue spiralled up into the air.

A small group of people milled happily about in the sunshine taking pictures and admiring the scenery. Hard at work over a big portable barbecue was a pretty girl in jeans and a checked shirt.

'Who are they all?' asked Caron, feeling suddenly shy as everyone turned to look at them.

'Tourists,' replied Ewan. 'Riding trail for the day. This is their lunch stop.'

A tall, capable-looking man came over. 'Hi, boss. You're just in time. Steaks are about done.'

'That's good, Bill,' nodded Ewan. 'We're about starved.'

He dismounted and went up to Caron. 'Planning on getting down? Or do you want to eat lunch up there?'

'Boss?' repeated Caron in a frozen voice. 'That man called you boss.'

She began to dismount and found his hands round her waist, lifting her down. 'You got a problem with that?' said Ewan softly, his lips inches from her own.

'You misled me,' accused Caron.

'You misled yourself,' he corrected her, still holding her a clear six inches off the ground.

'Put me down,' she said stiffly, her heart beating unreasonably fast. 'I'm quite capable of getting off a horse.' She paused and then added pointedly, 'Boss.'

'There's a trough over there,' said Ewan. 'That's where you usually end up when you start getting on your high horse.'

'On it, off it, what's the difference?' said Caron, realising suddenly, after all that unaccustomed exercise, how stiff and weary she felt. 'Nothing I could say would stop you from chucking me in it if you wanted to.'

'True,' he shrugged, leading their horses to the corral.

The steaks were delicious. Caron speared up the last piece of potato on her plate and sighed with contentment. 'That was truly wonderful,' she sighed. 'No wonder people pay thousands of pounds to come here for a holiday.'

Ewan looked at her in mock horror. 'You mean there's no food in England?'

'I mean there's nowhere in the world like this,' she said dreamily, leaning back against a sun-warmed rock. 'It's just beautiful.'

Ewan gazed around at the pines, the snow-capped mountains visible through a gap in the trees. 'Yes,' he agreed. 'It can really get to you.'

'And the air,' enthused Caron. 'It's so clear. It really sharpens your appetite.'

'Glad to hear it,' drawled Ewan. 'Does this mean from now on you're only going to be pining away for Neil between meals?'

Caron took his plate and hers and stood up abruptly. 'Are you always this beastly to people you hardly know?'

He rose to his feet, his eyes never leaving hers, and, reaching out his hands, drew her towards him. She felt that she ought to resist, but with Ewan Cameron that was no easy task.

He looked down at her silently for a moment. 'I could give you a smart answer to that, Caron, but out here I don't feel like it.'

'Amazing,' she said unsteadily.

The corners of his mouth quirked. 'You really—'

But whatever he had being going to say was cut short by the sudden arrival of the girl who had been doing the cooking. She gave Caron a hard, assessing stare and then turned to Ewan. 'Could you spare me a moment, honey? It's kinda important.'

And in a moment, it seemed, Caron was left on her own as Ewan walked away, deep in conversation with the pretty blonde. They soon passed out of sight behind some trees, and with an effort Caron stopped trying to see where they might have gone. It was a full thirty seconds before she realised she was staring at the two dirty plates as if she had never seen them before.

She saw Ewan and the girl come back, too. The way he clasped the girl's shoulder and the way she reached up and kissed him made Caron feel so suddenly and unexpectedly jealous that she wanted to hit out at something—preferably the nose on Ewan Cameron's beautifully sculpted face.

He was coming towards her now, grinning hugely, and Caron's jaw clenched. She turned on her heel and walked away to watch the tourists mount up. They were shouting with laughter at some of their number's more clumsy attempts to get on their horses.

'If I didn't know better,' said a soft voice she was beginning to know only too well, 'I would have staked my hat that just back there you were walking off in a huff about something.'

Caron glared at Ewan, who had come to stand next to her. 'I was not in a huff about anything.'

He smiled easily at her. 'Of course not. You're not the kind of woman to do anything by huffs.'

Caron opened her mouth and then closed it again. High spots of colour burned on her cheeks as she watched the tourists follow Bill back down the trail.

The girl was busy stacking all the picnic things in the back of a pick-up.

'Who's that girl?' Caron asked.

'Suzie,' replied Ewan laconically.

'She's a good cook,' said Caron shortly.

'Good with horses too,' remarked Ewan. 'And, unlike some people not a million miles from this spot,' he added, glancing at Caron, 'she's also extremely good-natured.'

Caron thought of the way the pair had looked at each other and gave way to the fierce jealousy in her heart. 'I'm surprised she isn't your housekeeper,' she said coolly.

Ewan's eyes glittered—but was it with amusement or malice? 'She's going to start right after you're gone,' he replied. 'Must say I can hardly wait.'

'I'm not at all surprised,' said Caron acidly, walking determinedly across to Suzie to help with the clearing-up. She was going to make friends with that girl if it killed her. Why should she pander to Ewan's ego by fighting in the slightest way over him? It would only reveal the attraction for him that she was trying so hard to smother.

In any case, it would do him nothing but good to discover, for maybe the first time in his life, that here was a woman who could take him or leave him.

With a pang she suddenly realised that if he kept his side of the bargain they had made the previous night she certainly would be leaving him. And it would be the day after tomorrow.

Making friends with Suzie proved to be slightly more difficult than Caron had hoped. The girl was cool almost to the point of rudeness. 'You've come all this way to discuss a will with Ewan?' she probed.

'Yes,' replied Caron, trying her best. 'There is apparently a lot of property involved and I thought it advisable to make a personal visit.'

'I'll bet,' said Suzie meaningfully.

Caron decided to lay her cards on the table. 'You're obviously very fond of Ewan.'

'Very,' the girl said simply.

'Well, don't look on me as a threat,' Caron told her, blindly drying a fork for the fourth time. 'I'm getting married on Saturday. This visit is purely business.'

Suzie turned to her with a puzzled look but whatever she had been going to say died on her lips as Ewan came up to them and tugged the girl's hair.

'Isn't it amazing, Suzie, to find a lawyer who can do the washing-up?'

'I've cleaned up after worse,' said Caron grimly.

Ewan smiled right into her eyes. 'I'm sure you have,' he replied.

He loaded the last box onto the pick-up, and shepherded Suzie into the driving seat. 'Drive safely, now,' he said affectionately.

'See you back at the ranch,' she called as the pick-up disappeared around a bend.

Caron turned and walked a little way up the trail. What was the matter with her? Why on earth should she be jealous of a girl's affection for a man she herself had known for less than twenty-four hours?

She sighed and mentally cursed herself for getting into a situation that she just couldn't seem to control. When was the last time Neil had shown her any affection? Not even at the beginning, she realised.

In fact, even before she had discovered what he was really like, he had never made her feel one tenth of the ridiculous, heart-stopping emotions that Ewan so easily unleashed in her. And now... She bit her lip.

She would just have to be more self-controlled, that was all. But it was easier said than done, especially when she felt as calm as an antelope on amphetamines. The sooner her stay here was over the better.

She stopped for a moment and gazed unseeingly at the mountains once more. 'That's better,' said Ewan. 'For a moment there I thought you were planning on walking back to the ranch.'

Caron whirled round to find him standing right behind her. 'Do you always stand this close to people?' she said unsteadily.

'What are you afraid of, Caron?' he asked gently.

'Nothing,' she quavered, trying hard to stop the feeling of mounting tension at his nearness. 'You're being ridiculous. What on earth should I be afraid of?'

'Yourself?' he suggested simply.

The idea took her so much by surprise that she gasped and took a step back.

'Careful,' said Ewan.

'What do you mean?' she demanded, ignoring his comment. 'Why should I be scared of me?'

'Because you won't face up to your life or the problems in it,' he answered, reaching out to her. 'Come on, hold my hand.'

'Don't be ridiculous,' she retorted, taking another step backwards and instantly experiencing the curious sensation of there being absolutely nothing under her foot.

In the split-second that she realised she had been on a rocky outcrop and was about to fall Ewan's hand shot out and dragged her back to safety.

'My God,' she whispered, looking at the dizzying drop from the safety of his arms. 'I could be down there now.'

'Mmm,' he replied. 'It's so far down, you'd probably still be on your way. Can't say I care too much for heights myself.'

'Me neither,' breathed Caron.

CHAPTER FIVE

EWAN pulled Caron further away from the cliff-edge and stared at her. 'Didn't you realise where you were?' he demanded.

'I wasn't even thinking about where I was,' she replied shakily.

He paled under his tan and drew a deep, ragged breath. 'You mean you come all the way out to some of the highest mountains in the world and you don't even think about the dangers of falling off one of them?'

Caron flicked a glance at him and then looked away quickly. Ewan was so angry that she suddenly felt breathless. 'I wasn't planning on going mountaineering,' she forced out. 'What's it to you anyway?'

He grabbed her by the shoulder and shook her a little. 'Don't be so stupid,' he grated. 'Like it or not, you're my responsibility now. And, however much I might feel the urge to drop you off the edge of a cliff, this is not the way I imagined saying goodbye to you.'

Caron wriggled from his grasp and, edging round him, walked a few steps back up the path to where she could no longer see the drop. 'The sensible thing to have done would have been to tell me I was standing on the edge of a precipice,' she said icily.

'The sensible thing to have done would have been not to stand there,' retorted Ewan. 'As it is, you walked straight past three warning signs. I thought you were looking at the scenery. I didn't realise you were so self-obsessed that you'd just walk off a precipice.'

'Shame I didn't,' snarled Caron. 'It would certainly have saved me from doing any more of your housework.'

There was a short silence and then Ewan strode towards her. The expression on his face made her quake inwardly but his hands grabbed her shoulders before she could even draw breath for her next retort. 'What...what do you think you are doing?' she gasped.

'I'm going to make you see sense for once if it's the last thing I do,' Ewan said grimly, lifting her and carrying her back to the edge of the cliff.

'I'm telling you,' Caron shouted, 'if you try anything silly and we get killed I'll sue you into the next world.'

'Good,' he snapped, clasping his arms around her waist and lifting her, kicking, higher up in the air. 'I'll see you in hell, then.'

She closed her eyes and swallowed hurriedly. 'You must be absolutely crazy,' she hissed. 'Just what are you trying to do?'

'Trying to make you live in the present instead of some secret world of your own,' he retorted. 'Now open those eyes and look around.'

'No,' Caron quavered. 'I won't. You're just being silly. And I'm not going to pander to your ridiculous demands.'

'I can still take a few more steps right to the cliff-edge,' he threatened.

'You don't like heights,' she replied.

'Neither do you,' he countered. 'And you're higher than me.'

'You're mad,' she breathed.

'Absolutely,' he agreed. 'Now open those eyes.'

Her eyes fluttered open. Ewan's arms were as steady as a rock around her and she knew she was perfectly safe, but still, being held a couple of feet off the ground near the edge of a cliff gave her the impression that she was almost floating in the air.

'Now,' he said, more gently. 'Tell me what you see.'

'Mountains,' she breathed. 'Whacking great beautiful mountains, covered in snow and reaching to the sky.'

'Anything else?' he questioned.

'Just the sky,' she said.

His arms tightened around her and he turned and walked a few paces before putting her down.

She stood looking at him for one long, still moment, drinking in a great lungful of mountain air to steady her nerves. Then she slapped him full in the face.

'How dare you do that to me?' she cried. 'How dare you? It was absolutely—'

'Unforgivable?' said Ewan.

She stared at him for a moment, watching the red marks of her fingers spread into his cheek.

'Why?' she asked. 'Why did you do it?'

He shrugged, putting his hand up to his face with a rueful expression. 'Because of that desperate look in your eyes, I guess.'

'I don't know what you mean,' she bit out.

He reached for her hand and numbly she let him take it. 'Come on,' he said quietly, leading her back down the trail to the corral. 'It's time we were getting back. I guess you didn't have too much sleep last night and you sure look like you could use some.'

She hung back a little, and, sensing the pressure on his hand, Ewan turned to look at her.

'What do you mean, desperate?' she forced out.

He looked at her assessingly and then smiled and shrugged. 'Most times when I look at you there's an expression in your eyes that animals have when they've been caught in a trap,' he said. 'But the difference is, I suspect, that your trap is of your own making.'

'It's none—' began Caron angrily.

He lifted his hand. 'I know, I know. It's none of my business and will I kindly keep out. But you're a beautiful woman, Caron, and I can't see you putting your head in a noose without trying to do something about it.'

'Like throwing me off a cliff?' she snapped.

'Like trying to show you that a world exists outside the little box you've constructed for your life.'

'Well, thank you, Doctor,' she retorted.

He gave her arm a little shake. 'Don't you want to know the good news?'

'Is there any?' she said as flippantly as she could.

He tugged a stray lock from her tumbled mass of hair and flashed her a grin. 'For someone looking forward to what is supposed to be the happiest day of your life you sure are short on cheerfulness at times.'

'Next time I come to see you on a business visit I'll wear a clown's outfit,' she retorted acidly.

'That might not be such a crazy idea,' he said idly. 'You already have the big false smile.'

Caron wrenched her hand away from his. 'You really are the limit,' she spat. 'I don't think I've ever met a man as insulting as you. Ever.'

He gave a little mock bow. 'I'll take that as a compliment, ma'am.'

'You can take it any way you like,' she forced out. 'I just wish sometimes you'd also take a running jump.'

He threw her a sideways glance, his eyes twinkling. 'Only sometimes?' he drawled. 'My, but I must be going up in your estimation.' He smiled outright then at the way her eyes narrowed, but before she could say anything he turned and walked off, back down the trail to the corral.

She watched him go, the way his shirt emphasised his wide shoulders, his long-legged stride, seemingly so slow yet surprisingly fast if you had to keep up with it.

A sudden picture of him scaring off the bear flashed vividly across her mind and with a cross between a gulp and a sob she found herself running down the path after him. 'No, Ewan, wait for me!' she shouted, unable to keep up her cool façade any longer.

He turned and waited until she came up to him, watching her with an expression that was completely unreadable.

'I just—' She paused and breathed deeply. He said nothing, just gazed at her with those eyes which saw so disconcertingly far into her heart, and she thought hurriedly of some excuse to cover her lamentable lapse of dignity.

'I just . . .' she attempted again. 'I just wanted to know what the good news was,' she said in a rush. 'You know, you said there was some, after shaking me up and down on the edge of that cliff.'

He suppressed a grin and stared up at the sky before looking down to meet her gaze once more.

'It's not very earth-shattering,' he said at last.

'Tell me,' she urged.

He shrugged. 'Well, when I told you to open your eyes you looked up at the mountains, and when I asked you what else you could see you looked even higher up. That must mean you have some optimism in your soul.'

'Trick psychology,' she sniffed.

'Maybe,' he conceded with a smile. 'But you never once looked down.'

*   *   *

The forest seemed hushed in the afternoon sunshine. The bird-calls were muted and the scent of pine lay heavy on the still air. 'It's like being in a cathedral,' said Caron quietly, gazing in awe at the soaring trees.

'Better,' Ewan corrected her. 'It's all alive, and it's certainly been here longer than anything a man could build.'

She gazed at the corral and the spot where they had eaten their barbecue lunch. Apart from the sturdy fencing, and a well-camouflaged little wooden privy, the glade beside it looked as though no one had been there for years.

'I must say your lot keep everything incredibly tidy,' she remarked.

'My lot?' he repeated.

'Your employees,' she amended, with an attempt at light sarcasm. 'You know, the people you pay to clean up after you. Like me, for instance.'

Ewan glanced at her. 'I wouldn't say any of my employees were the least like you,' he replied. 'They're all perfectly sane, happy people.'

'Thanks,' she snapped. 'But I was perfectly sane and happy until I came out here.'

'I guess so,' he drawled sardonically. 'So, in that case, why aren't you at home gazing lovingly into Neil's eyes and practising how to say your wedding vows?'

Caron had an instant picture of the last time she had stared into Neil's eyes. It had been the night she had found him in bed with his mistress, Kate Andrews, and had discovered the enormity of the trap she had fallen into. It was a moment she would never forget, not as long as she lived.

Caron thrust the memory out of her mind and looked numbly up at Ewan. 'What did you say?' she stumbled.

'Something not terribly important, I think,' he said softly. He leant on the corral fence and rubbed the nose of his bay horse. 'What does he do, this Neil?'

'He's a solicitor,' said Caron shortly.

'Well off?' probed Ewan.

'Not really,' she replied. 'Why? Do you think I'm after him for his money?'

Ewan shrugged. 'It may have passed through my mind,' he said easily.

She coloured up and turned away from him with an effort. If only he knew the truth. But that was something she couldn't tell anyone.

'What's wrong, Caron?' he said at last. 'Sometimes it helps to tell someone who's not involved. I'd like to help, if I can.'

She turned to him with a thud of hope and then the enormity of what was facing her made her shake her head suddenly. 'No,' she said at last.

He looked at her assessingly. 'Want to fight your own battles, huh?'

'Something like that,' she conceded abruptly.

He tipped her chin up with a gentle forefinger. 'Why don't you just admit you made a mistake and call the wedding off? No one will think any the worse of you. In fact, it takes more guts to do something like that than just to go along with a situation you don't like, but are too scared to duck out of.'

Caron glared at him and pulled his hand away. 'Sometimes it takes even more "guts", as you call it, to follow something through.'

His eyebrows lifted, and she bit her lip. She shouldn't have said anything, dammit. At this rate Ewan would have the whole story out of her before she could even blink.

'So you're marrying him out of a sense of duty,' he drawled. 'My, my, what a lucky man he must be.'

'You're putting words into my mouth,' she snapped.

'Guess they're the right ones, though,' he replied.

'Don't be ridiculous,' she retorted.

'I don't think I'm being ridiculous,' he said calmly. 'You're the one talking about having to get married, and yet you've flown six thousand miles just to avoid it.'

'Stop it,' she whispered furiously.

But Ewan was relentless. 'And, in any case, what kind of duty is it we're talking about here? Duty to dear old Neil? Or is this wedding just to seal some sort of feudal family contract?'

'You're jumping to conclusions,' said Caron desperately.

'Me?' he replied. 'I'm just a rank amateur in that respect. But you . . .' He shrugged. 'You jump to so many conclusions about people you could probably enter the Olympics.'

'I do not,' she breathed furiously.

'What about Neil, then?' he probed. 'Did you jump to a lot of romantic conclusions about him and then find he wasn't quite the shining knight you wanted him to be?'

'N-not really,' she stammered.

He raised an eyebrow. She lifted her chin and stared at him as steadily as she could. 'I'm going back to England on Tuesday,' she began. 'And I shall marry Neil on Saturday.'

'I hope you'll be very happy,' he said, and something in his eyes made her heart turn over.

'You can come to the wedding if you like,' she said lightly, and then, remembering how he had misled her about being the boss of the ranch, added challengingly, 'You do have a suit, don't you?'

He smiled lazily at her. 'Somewhere, I expect.'

The mare came pushing up beside the bay for attention and Caron reached out a hand to rub the white blaze between the horse's eyes. Anything for an excuse not to look Ewan in the face.

'I'm sorry,' she muttered at last. 'I don't know what's got into me. I didn't mean to insult you about the suit.'

'You didn't,' he said easily.

She glanced up at him and gave a small smile. 'No. I don't suppose I did. It would take a lot to upset you, Ewan Cameron.'

'Less than you might think,' he said calmly. 'You should see me when my favourite ice hockey team loses.'

Caron smiled weakly. 'It's just that, out here, it's difficult to imagine you in any sort of formal setting.'

His eyes, full of an amusement that she couldn't quite place, slid to hers. 'Are you coming out with another of those amazing insults of yours?'

She swallowed. 'No. I merely meant—'

'Yes?' he prompted.

Caron licked her lips and looked around at the trees and the soaring mountains. 'It's just that you seem such a part of all this.'

He followed her gaze. 'They move sometimes, you know.'

She stared at him in astonishment. 'What?'

'The mountains,' he said. 'On a real hot afternoon the heat haze makes them shimmer. And if you're in Calgary it's even more noticeable. They seem to change their distance from day to day. Sometimes they can look real close, and other days—' he shrugged '—it's as if they've retreated so far away you'll never get among them again.'

'Could you imagine living without them?' she said softly.

He shook his head. 'For ever? No.' He turned and smiled at her. 'A man needs to know the things he loves are there when he wants them.'

'I wouldn't know,' muttered Caron, her gaze dropping to the floor. The silence stretched out between them like widening ripples in a still pond.

This was no good at all, she thought desperately. She lifted her head with a jerk and switched on a full-beam smile. 'Still,' she said, 'it's nice that it's kept so clean around here.' She sounded like her mother commenting on the state of her flat and she reddened. The tension between herself and Ewan was almost tangible.

She had to say something to keep the conversation cool and detached, but as she gazed at him her mind went completely blank, except for the disconcerting thought that despite his obviously hard job he had really long, beautiful fingers. She resisted, with an effort, the urge to reach out for them and ask for the comfort she wanted so desperately.

Then Ewan flashed her a look that was anything but cool or detached and for some reason she found herself folding her arms, as if to ward him off.

But when he spoke it was as if he had decided to help her keep up her façade. 'Being tidy is just sensible,' he said neutrally.

'Otherwise you'd have bears scavenging around, I suppose,' agreed Caron with an effort. 'And even the smallest piece of litter could cause a fire.'

Ewan turned her to face him and she trembled at his touch. 'The most amazing things can set off a fire, Caron.'

She stared up at him and hugged her arms tighter round her body. 'Yes,' she replied with a mental struggle. 'A little bit of sunshine, some warmth magnified out of all proportion and before you know where you are the whole forest is on fire.'

His hands were cupping her face now, the sensation of those beautiful fingers against her skin sending a shiver down her spine. 'That kind of fire is almost impossible to fight,' he said softly.

'Y-you just need good control to begin with,' she stammered.

'In this case,' he told her, 'good control is the last thing you need.'

'No, Ewan, I can't,' she gasped as his hand slid down around her shoulders and drew her close.

'When something goes up in flames,' he said as her arms reached falteringly around his neck, 'there is no such word as "can't".'

Nothing could have prepared her for the searing sensuality of his embrace as they stood alone in the forest. Heat surged through her body as lips moved over hers, and there was nothing she wanted more when he guided her down on to the forest floor.

Every single piece of her was alive to him, and her body refused to obey the desperate signals which her mind was sending out.

Silently she watched him strip off his shirt and lay it as a pillow under her head. 'Your hair is like a pool of gold,' he murmured as his fingers traced a path down her throat and over the soft silk of her shirt-front. He undid the buttons, slid the fabric aside, and then all

words ceased as his mouth moved to caress her breasts
through the satin material of her bra, cupping them with
gentle fingers.

Was this real, or was it a dream that was stronger than
reality? Her fingers stroked through Ewan's hair and
down to the strong column of his neck. This could not
be her, responding to him as if she were on fire. No man
had ever made her feel like this. She was floating,
drowning, suffused with wanting.

And then, as awakening and unwelcome as the icy
water he had thrown at her that morning, a sudden
picture of Ewan kissing Suzie's cheerful face flashed
across her brain, and cold common sense seeped into
her heart. 'Ewan,' she pleaded breathlessly.

His eyes turned to engulf her but she looked away
quickly. If she returned his gaze she would be lost. 'I...we
can't do this,' she stumbled. 'We—'

His chest was brown, the sunlight giving it a polished
sheen. Instinctively her hand reached out to touch his
arm, her fingers trailing over the warm, silky hardness
of his muscles. Something inside her seemed to jolt and
she closed her eyes hurriedly. Something was happening
to her that she was almost powerless to prevent.

'This is wrong,' she forced out.

'No,' he whispered, his lips fluttering once more
against her throat.

'You...' she began again.

His face was only inches above hers. 'I what?' he said
softly.

'You can't do this,' she repeated with an effort.
'It's...wrong. And you know it.'

His eyes met hers with sudden clarity. 'Wrong for you?
Or wrong because you've promised yourself to a man
you don't love?'

Caron struggled to sit up, Ewan moving with her, his arms about her. 'That's outrageous,' she gasped, trying ineffectually to do up her buttons.

Ewan gently knocked her hand away from her shirt-front. 'Here, let me do that. Your fingers are shaking too much and you've got all the wrong holes.'

Her hands dropped and she lifted her chin as he undid her shirt once more. But instead of refastening it his hands slid inside and he pulled her to him. 'Your skin is like satin,' he muttered. 'I don't think I could ever get tired of touching it.'

She gasped as he pulled her closer, but he stopped her mouth with a kiss and she knew that she was falling for a man that she could never have. With an effort she wrenched herself away. 'I—I'm n-not going to respond to you,' she stammered. 'I won't.'

'Like you didn't respond just now, you mean?' he enquired.

'I told you,' she forced out, trembling. 'It's just some sort of silly sexual chemistry.'

He smiled lazily at her. 'So what's wrong with that? If this is silly sexual chemistry, then I have to admit I'm all for it.'

Tears welled in her eyes. 'I can't,' she whispered. 'I just can't do this.'

He gazed silently at her for a second and then pulled her close and hugged her. 'Maybe you can't now,' he murmured against her hair. 'And I won't force you. But you and I both know that the day will come soon when you will lie down in my arms.'

'No,' she whispered with an effort, her heart surging at his words.

Silence surrounded them for a moment and then, with a wry smile, Ewan buttoned her up as if she were some sort of shop-window mannequin.

'Apart from anything else,' she said stiffly, not daring to look him in the eye, 'there's Suzie to consider as well.'

He gazed at her with a puzzled expression. 'Suzie?' he repeated.

'Don't think I didn't see you kissing her earlier,' she accused, more vehemently than she had meant, and then added more softly, 'I know she loves you.'

Ewan opened his mouth and closed it again. 'Guess I can't deny it,' he said blandly. 'And then, of course, there's Neil, though I have to say I've not had the pleasure of seeing you kiss him yet.'

Caron scrambled to her feet. 'You really are just about the limit,' she snapped. 'Do you know that?'

Ewan nodded and smiled into her eyes. 'Guess I do. But it's nice to be reminded of it occasionally.'

She brushed off her jeans furiously. 'How dare you make judgements about something you know nothing about?'

'You made the judgement,' said Ewan. 'Everything you say, and don't say, about Neil shows that. You don't love him. You don't even think about him.'

Caron glared at him. 'You're just a predator,' she burst out. 'And you don't give a damn, do you?' She blinked back fresh tears, and took another step back from him. 'You just hope to get what you can out of people and damn everyone's feelings but your own, don't you?'

He reached for his shirt and pulled it on slowly, his eyes never leaving her face for a moment. 'I've never "preyed" on a woman in my life,' he said evenly. 'You're just blaming me because you can't cope with your own feelings.'

'I can cope perfectly well with my feelings,' replied Caron wildly.

'Is that why you're crying?' he said gently.

'I'm not crying. I've just got something in my eye,' she lied fiercely.

He gave her a knowing look and then pulled his gaze away from hers and rasped his fingers thoughtfully along his jawline. 'We'd better get one thing straight,' he said at last. 'I like women, respect that different way they have of looking at things. But you—' He shrugged.

'I what?' she said furiously. 'You mean I'm fair game: far from home, no friends, no money and you just can't resist moving in.'

He stood up and moved towards her. 'Like this, you mean?' he said softly, a dangerous glint in his eyes.

'Keep away from me,' she said fiercely. 'Or so help me I'll—'

'You'll what?' he said. 'If I was as much of a "predator" as you claim, I could do what I liked and there'd be no one within five miles to hear, or even care.'

Caron swallowed. 'You wouldn't dare.'

'If I'm as bad as you paint me I would,' he said softly.

Caron stared into his eyes, and saw a spark of humour flare in them. 'You're just winding me up,' she whispered.

He shook his head slightly. 'No, Caron. You are the one who is doing the winding. You are the one who is so stretched with nerves that she can't even recognise her own feelings.'

'My feelings are my own affair,' Caron flashed.

'Of course,' he nodded, walking off to their horses and leading them out of the corral.

She stood watching him, indecisive about what to do next, and then, on an impulse, hurried after him. 'What do you mean "of course"?' she demanded. 'What makes you the expert on my feelings? You know absolutely nothing about them.'

'Caron,' he said, 'I met you almost eighteen hours ago. And I feel like I've known you for eighteen years. I know how to make you laugh. And I know how to make you madder than hell.'

'You don't know anything,' she contradicted him, fighting down the impulse to brush some pine needles from the back of his shirt.

For a moment he just stood there in silence. Then he said quietly, 'I also know how to make love to you, Caron.'

She gathered up the reins with trembling fingers and mounted her horse. 'That was just silliness,' she said fiercely. 'And it's not going to lead to anything else. So don't get the wrong idea.'

He smiled up at her and for one horrified instant she thought she was going to smile back. 'You're the one who generally seems to get the wrong idea, Caron,' he said gently.

He turned to his own horse and swung himself easily up into the saddle. 'In fact, if you didn't have such pre-conceived ideas when you met people, then you wouldn't fall so flat on your face afterwards when you discovered the truth.'

Caron lifted her chin and began to ride off. Once again she could think of no suitably crushing reply, because once again he was absolutely right. Damn him, damn him, damn him.

Ewan looked speculatively at her straight back as she took the trail home and then, smiling, cantered easily after her.

* * *

The house seemed to welcome them when they returned. Ewan dismounted then lifted Caron down as she slithered wearily off the saddle. The effect of his nearness was almost overwhelming. For a moment she thought he was going to kiss her again, and her whole body trembled.

But he merely set her on her feet and looked down at her for a long moment.

'Can I use your telephone?' she asked, refusing to look him directly in the face.

He nodded expressionlessly. 'Of course,' he said. 'I'm going down to the stables so your call will be quite private.'

She nodded briefly. 'Thanks.'

Caron watched him re-mount the tall bay and gather the mare's reins. 'Thank you for today,' she said at last.

'All of today?' he said gently.

Caron stared up at his face, half in shade from his stetson, and swallowed hard. 'I'm still going to marry Neil,' she replied in a rush.

He nodded consideringly. 'Because you love him? Or out of your sense of duty?'

She opened her mouth but no words came out, and she ran blindly into the house. The door banged behind her and she half expected Ewan to come straight in after her—to argue with her, tell her she was wrong, to order her not to marry Neil. But as the silence lengthened she knew that she had been grasping at straws.

In a few days from now Ewan would forget all about her, would probably be taking Suzie for rides in the forest, while she would marry Neil and try to keep her part of a bargain she had never wanted to make.

She looked around at the kitchen she had spent so long cleaning and tried to think of what was going on at home now. Her parents had seemed disconcerted, to say the least, when she had announced that she had a last-minute business trip. But they had given her all their support when they'd realised just how nervous she was feeling. Neither of them, she knew, cared much for Neil.

Her normal life, everything that she knew, all seemed so far away. So unreal. Caron sighed and looked at her watch. It would be about nine or ten at night in England now. Maybe even at this late stage she could get Neil to see sense and set her free.

It was Kate who answered the phone, and Caron's hand tightened on the receiver. 'Just a minute,' came the low, seductive voice. 'He's in bed at the moment.'

Caron breathed deeply and resisted the urge to rip the telephone cord out of the wall and hurl the instrument through the window.

Eventually Neil came on the phone. Caron summoned up her courage. 'I know we made a bargain,' she said coldly, 'but I hardly see why you need Kate to rub my nose in it.'

'I don't know what you mean,' he replied blandly. 'Kate is my secretary and she and I were going over some reports.'

Caron counted to five. 'You can go over as many reports as you like,' she bit out. 'I don't give a damn, and I'm calling off the deal we made. I must have been out of my mind to agree to it.'

'Really?' Neil's tone was bored.

'Yes, really,' snapped Caron. 'Whatever you said, I am just not going through with this wedding.' She breathed deeply. It hadn't been so difficult after all.

Then Neil spoke and she could feel the ice slide through her veins once more. 'Of course we're going through with the wedding,' he replied in that reasonable tone she had begun to hate. 'Think of all the fuss and bother your parents have been to. Never mind the expense.'

'They'd rather cancel it than see me unhappy,' forced out Caron.

'Oh, I don't think they'll cancel it,' replied Neil. 'Because you obviously still haven't fully read the copies I gave you of the rather nasty incriminating documents I have about your father. But when you do you'll definitely be at the church as planned on Saturday afternoon with a very big smile indeed stitched on your face.'

There was click and Caron was left holding the phone, listening numbly to a silence that was considerably longer than a mere six thousand miles.

CHAPTER SIX

CARON sat limply on the sofa and picked unseeingly at a loose thread in one of its big, squashy cushions. Leaning back with a sigh, she thought of the trap Neil had sprung. He had taken his time about it, she realised; played her like a salmon on a line. But then to him she was a prize worth having. Or rather, she thought wryly, her trust fund was.

He had seemed so nice at first, so right, taking her out for the expensive treats she liked. She had been dazzled by him, she knew that now, but when they had had that row, over Kate, he had shown her those damning papers and she had caved in to every one of his demands.

Neil had been right; she could not expose her father. She could not even discuss it with him for fear of sparking off another heart attack. The noose was closing tight about her and however she pored over those papers there was simply no way out. And he'd had no need to put a set of them in her bag—Caron knew them all off by heart.

She was so tired. So desperately tired. She hadn't slept properly for days. But then she had been so naïve. So unforgivably stupid. How could she ever have thought him attractive when the prospect of marrying him now was nothing less than repulsive?

Caron stared blearily up at the ceiling. It was no use. She could sit here for a year and still not find an escape route. Her eyelids drooped and within five minutes she was fast asleep.

* * *

The nightmare was a familiar one: she was in a burning building and Neil barred every escape route. 'No!' she yelled. 'Get out of my way!' But strong hands held her and she struggled wildly. 'I won't do it. I won't.'

'You don't have to do anything,' a quiet voice told her, and Caron snapped open her eyes to find herself sitting up in bed, Ewan's face inches from her own.

'You were having a nightmare,' he told her. 'But you're quite safe. Relax.'

Caron laid her head on his shoulder and felt his hand stroke her hair. 'It was awful,' she muttered. 'Just awful.'

'Sounded a beauty,' he agreed. 'Want to talk about it?'

She shook her head quickly. Too quickly. 'No.' She felt his hand stop on her hair, the easy intimacy of the moment icing over. She pulled back a little. 'I'm sorry if I disturbed you.'

He shrugged. 'You didn't. And I don't exactly have any neighbours to bang on the walls.'

'That's true,' she said stiffly, the nearness of his body jerking her pulse rate into a sudden syncopated rhythm. She looked around at the softly lit bedroom and then back at Ewan's face. 'I don't understand,' she muttered. 'I can't remember going to bed. The last thing I remember is...'

'What?' prompted Ewan.

'Making a phone call,' she said slowly.

'To Neil?' he asked.

She lifted her chin. 'If you want to know, yes. Why? Will you be wanting me to work extra hours to pay the telephone bill?'

'Not a bad idea,' he mused.

She glared at him. 'Your hold over me disappears the day the banks open.' She looked at the clock and then

back at him. 'Which is now tomorrow. So even if you
don't keep your part of the bargain I shall still be leaving,
even if I have to walk all the way back to town myself.'

Ewan stood up with easy grace and her eyes widened.
She had forgotten that she was alone with him in the
house. And that it was miles from anywhere. As he stood
over her, seeming to take up the whole room, she realised
just how much at his mercy she was.

He looked down at her thoughtfully and then said,
'You know, when I take you into town tomorrow I think
I'll do a little shopping. I'm going to buy that Neil of
yours a wedding present.'

'You wouldn't—' began Caron, and then, seeing the
glint in his eye, she stopped and abruptly asked instead,
'What?'

He gazed speculatively at her. 'Of course, I'm not sure
the shop will have it in stock, but I guess I could always
get one from a park ranger.'

'What?' repeated Caron hotly.

'A tranquilliser gun,' replied Ewan equably. 'I'm sure
you must have seen one on a TV documentary. They're
very useful when you want to get up close to something
wild and unpredictable.

'So when Neil wants to get close to you he can just
hide behind a bush or something and take aim.'

Caron glared at him. 'He's not going to get much sense
out of me if I'm lying unconscious on the floor.'

Ewan smiled right into her eyes. 'Would that make
any difference?'

Furious, she opened her mouth but he just carried
right on. 'I mean, common sense doesn't really seem to
be your strong suit right at this moment, does it? And
with one of those guns to protect him he could easily

attach a homing device to you. So if you did decide to run off again he'd know exactly where you'd gone.'

Caron knelt up in bed and grabbed a pillow to throw at him. 'That's absolutely outrageous!' she yelled. 'You're only saying that because it's just the sort of stupid macho idea that would appeal to a man like you.'

Ewan leant down and tipped up her chin. 'Not quite, sweetheart,' he said quietly. 'You see, if I proposed to a woman, the last thing she'd want to do is run away.'

Caron realised she was gripping the pillow so tightly that her fingers ached, and her eyes dropped under his unrelenting gaze. There was absolutely no way she'd ever get the better of this man in a verbal sparring match.

She grasped hold of the fingers that were still under her chin, but smilingly he slid them from her grasp. 'You planning on challenging me to a pillow fight?' he enquired.

'Certainly not,' she snapped, lifting the pillow to put it back behind her. Her mouth opened in surprise. 'What's this?' she demanded, realising that she was dressed in just her briefs and a strange T-shirt. 'I've never seen this in my life before,' she added, picking at the smooth cotton.

'Oh, that,' said Ewan. 'That's one of my T-shirts.'

'I've got a perfectly good nightdress under my pillow,' responded Caron tartly, and then stopped, her lips parting in surprise at the implications of what must have happened.

Ewan sat down the bed again and took one of her hands. 'Yes, I saw that thing,' he agreed. 'Looked more like an instrument of torture than a nightgown. Reminded me of something my granny used to scare birds with. All high neck and three million buttons.'

'Ewan,' she said, dangerously quiet.

He glanced at her. 'Of course, I have a fairly wide selection of T-shirts,' he said innocently. 'If you don't like that one I guess we could spend the rest of the night having some sort of fashion parade. Might be fun.'

She pulled her hand away. 'I don't believe you took my clothes off while I was asleep,' she said angrily. 'I just don't believe even you could stoop so low.'

He gazed steadily into her eyes. 'I could have stooped much lower than that if I had wanted to. And if you had been awake,' he added silkily, 'you would have enjoyed every moment of it.'

'That's despicable,' she stormed. 'You just took advantage of me.'

He reached out for her hands and held them fast. 'When I came home this evening you were stretched out snoring on the sofa.'

'I was not snoring!' Caron snapped. She looked at him horrified. 'Was I?'

He grinned slowly. 'Cute little snores. Like a puppy snuffling.'

'You still haven't given me an adequate explanation as to why I am wearing your T-shirt,' she said icily.

'Uh-oh,' smiled Ewan. 'Back to solicitor mode, I see. I might have known that acting like a human being wouldn't last.'

'That's not fair,' breathed Caron furiously. 'You took my clothes off while I was asleep and I want to know why.'

He gazed at her steadily. 'As I was saying,' he replied, 'before I was so rudely interrupted...' He paused as if waiting for her to rush in once more, and then continued, 'I came in this evening and saw you fast asleep on the sofa.'

'Why didn't you just leave me alone?'

He smiled at her. 'Because you looked about as comfortable as a snake on a hot plate.'

'Thank you,' muttered Caron.

Ewan shrugged. 'Well, you did. Your clothes were all rucked up and you looked like you were about to fall off the sofa any minute.'

He paused before adding gently, 'You looked exhausted, Caron, as if all the fight had been beaten out of you.'

His eyes were like deep, inky pools of water in the soft light. And it would be the easiest thing in the world to fall right into them, thought Caron. Her lips parted with unspoken desire as she gazed at the planes and curves of his face. He had to be the most handsome man she had ever seen in her life.

With a start she realised that he was gazing at her just as closely. This was ridiculous. You couldn't fall for a man you had known for only a few hours. Could you? She thought of Suzie and shook her head quickly. She should never have come here. Never.

She glared at him. 'Why don't you just mind your own business for a change?'

He smiled right into her eyes and upturned her hands on the patchwork quilt. 'Next minute,' he said conversationally, 'you're going to tell me you hate me.'

'How did you guess?' she snapped.

Gently he lifted her right wrist to his lips and kissed it. 'Do you mean that?' he whispered huskily.

'Absolutely,' she choked out as a little shiver of heat spread under her skin.

'Totally?' he asked, bending his head to the pulse-point on her left wrist.

'Completely,' she muttered.

'You don't seem too sure,' he replied. 'In fact, if I were to go on what your body is telling me, I'd say you were lying.'

'I'm getting married in five days' time,' whispered Caron. 'This is just not right.'

'Getting married to Neil is just not right, you mean,' Ewan corrected her.

'You don't even know him,' she snapped. 'And who are you to judge? I bet you've never wanted to marry anyone in your life.'

'Neither have you,' said Ewan quietly. 'You just want someone to keep you in silk suits and expensive lipsticks.'

'And you don't want to be tied down—don't tell me,' she retorted. 'I said you were a predator and I was right. I bet you've never told anyone, ever, that you love them.'

There was a light in his eyes now that made the breath catch in Caron's throat. This time she had gone too far. 'You know something?' said Ewan quietly—too quietly. 'I'll bet you never have either.'

He reached up to her heavy mass of hair and slowly ran his fingers through it, taking out the pins holding it in place one by one. 'Don't,' she said, shivering.

'Marrying a man you don't love is fairly despicable, wouldn't you say?' murmured Ewan, pressing her back onto the pillows and kissing the hollow of her throat.

'Now you're the one who's jumping to conclusions,' she rasped, fighting to hang onto her sanity as his hands slid up under the thin cotton T-shirt.

'He terrifies the life out of you,' said Ewan, his body dangerously close to hers. 'The very thought of him gives you nightmares. What kind of a hold has he got over you?'

He paused. 'Are you marrying him for his money? Or is there a much more old-fashioned reason than that?'

Caron stared at him in shock. 'You mean am I pregnant?' she gasped.

He gazed levelly at her. 'Well, are you?'

'Don't be ridiculous,' she burst out. 'We haven't even—'

She stopped abruptly. This man was too damn shrewd by half. But confiding in him would mean exposing her father. And that was something she couldn't even bear to face in her own heart, never mind laying it all out to be filleted by Ewan's razor-sharp mind.

'I can't tell you about this,' she muttered at last, her eyes shining with unshed tears. 'I can't.'

She rolled away from him with a sob, and wrapped her arms tightly around her. 'What do you care, anyway? After all, in a few hours I'll be out of your life and you can go back to your horses and your beloved mountains.'

And Suzie, she wanted to add. But pride would not let her.

The mattress creaked as Ewan rolled over onto his back and sighed. 'Caron, I don't pretend to be the most intelligent man in the universe, but it doesn't take Einstein to figure out that you are being coerced into doing something you do not want to do.'

'That's not true. It's my decision,' Caron asserted.

'Well, then, why don't I just call up the men in white coats to come and measure you up for a strait-jacket now? It would save everyone, Neil included, a deal of heartache. Because it is obviously a decision you are not too happy about, to say the least.'

She turned to face him. 'Don't do this to me, Ewan. Please don't. Maybe you're right. Maybe...' She shrugged, and then whispered, 'Maybe I don't always see eye to eye with Neil. But I have to marry him, and that's all there is to it.'

His hand slid around her throat, his fingers stroking the nape of her neck, pulling her towards him. 'This is wrong,' she forced out. 'You know it is.'

'I know all I need to know,' he rasped. 'I know that I want you like I've never wanted any other woman. I know from the look in your eyes that you feel the same way.'

His smile was bitter as she trembled at the touch of his fingers on her skin. 'I'm not Neil, Caron, and I won't force you. But then,' he shrugged, 'you and I both know that I won't need to.'

He kissed her then, his lips hard on hers, his caress a statement of possession, a deep primeval promise that she would be no other man's woman.

And then he pulled back, his finger stroking her tear-wet eyelashes, her swollen lips. 'You can't escape from your feelings, Caron,' he said softly. 'And it's best not to try.' His hand dropped away and he swung himself off the bed.

She watched him go, aching for him, and yet too afraid to tell him the truth. 'Ewan?' she whispered. 'I have to marry him, Ewan. And it's not what you think.'

He paused at the door, but he left without turning around.

Caron knew by the way the light was shining through her curtains that it was nearly noon when she woke later that day. She had not slept well and her head was throbbing, every overstretched nerve-ending in her body demanding release from the tension that Ewan's caresses had built up in her. A demand that only he could fulfil.

She ran a hand distractedly through the tangle of her hair and slipped on her robe. Maybe if she cleaned something else, she thought vaguely, really used up all

her energy, then she would feel so tired that she would
be able to sleep properly for once.

She padded into the living room and looked at it
wearily. It was in nowhere near as bad a state as the
kitchen had been, and it wouldn't take half as long to
smarten up. But at least it was something to occupy her.

'You look like Napoleon surveying a map of Russia.'

Caron whirled round to find Ewan standing in the
kitchen doorway, his fingers curled around a mug of
coffee. 'Really?' she forced out, trying hard to match
his oh, so light tone. 'I was merely wondering how long
it was going to take to clean this place up.'

His eyes slanted as he smiled, she noticed. 'Guess that's
what Napoleon thought too,' he remarked.

She pulled the tie of her robe more tightly around her.
'Ewan, if I'm going tomorrow I really think we ought
to discuss those papers. I mean—' she gave a little shrug
'—it is really why I came all the way out here.'

He looked at her consideringly. 'I have to go down to
the stables now, but we can look at them together later,
if you like.'

It was not until after he had gone and she had
showered, dressed and eaten breakfast-cum-lunch that
she remembered that she had used up all Ewan's meagre
supply of cleaning materials on the kitchen. She looked
out at the stables and, on a whim, pulled open the back
door.

A walk in the sunshine would do her good, and maybe
Ewan would lend her a car to go to the shops.

The stables looked much bigger the closer she got,
and as she saw a girl and a man leaning on a paddock
rail her steps slowed. Maybe this wasn't such a good
idea. But before she could turn tail and flee she saw Ewan
looking straight at her and beckoning her over.

Suzie was staring at her with a troubled face and Caron could not return her gaze. The only person who seemed blithely unaware of the tension was Ewan. 'Given yourself the afternoon off, I see,' he said lightly.

'Actually I came in search of supplies,' she said stiffly.

Suzie stared from one to the other. 'Look, Ewan,' she said, 'I've got that appointment and I just can't miss it.'

Ewan flicked her a glance. 'OK,' he said easily. 'Want to borrow the pick-up?'

The girl's solemn face broke into a smile. 'Great.'

He turned and kissed her on the cheek. 'See you tonight, honey.'

Suzie gave his cheek a brief pat and, after giving Caron a piercing glance, walked away quickly.

Ewan turned to Caron. 'How about you?' he asked. 'Want to go out tonight? Sample some down-home entertainment?'

Caron counted to a very slow ten as she watched Suzie hurry off. 'You have got to be joking,' she then replied.

Ewan raised an eyebrow. 'Meaning?' he queried.

'Meaning you treat that girl appallingly,' she snapped.

Ewan gazed at her innocently. 'I've just lent her my pick-up and I'm seeing her tonight. What more could a girl want?'

'Some meaningful affection, instead of being treated like some toy, a doll to be picked up and put down just when you feel like it,' replied Caron bitterly.

'You talking from personal experience?' drawled Ewan.

'Don't you dare talk to me about Neil!' retorted Caron. 'You're just as bad as he is!'

'Not just you wait a minute...' began Ewan.

'I wouldn't wait a millisecond for an explanation from you,' breathed Caron. 'Because it wouldn't mean a damned thing.'

Ewan was standing close to her now. Dangerously close. 'I'm not sure I like being talked about in the same breath as your precious Neil,' he said softly.

'Better get used to it,' she retorted. 'Because you are absolutely two of a kind. You want to have a girl on the side, and you don't care what you do to get her. All *you've* stopped short of so far is blackmail—unlike Neil. But I expect it's only a matter of time.'

She stopped abruptly, realising, with a burning wash of shame, that she had told him everything that she had been so determined to keep secret.

His fingers brushed her cheek. 'Blackmail? What on earth could you have done that he can use to make you marry him?'

She lifted her chin angrily. 'I haven't done anything. It was my—' She bit off the last word and stared at him silently. What her father had done was his secret. She couldn't give it away. Not to anyone. 'Nothing that concerns you,' she began again. 'I've told you, I'm simply not going to talk about it.'

'Oh, but I think you are,' he said quietly. 'You are going to tell me everything about this charming fiancé of yours.'

'What are you going to do?' she challenged. 'Get out the rack and thumbscrews?'

He shrugged. 'Have you dusted them yet?'

Caron gasped. 'You think you can make a joke out of everything, don't you? Including me. Well, just back off, Ewan, because this is none of your business and I'm going to handle it in my own way.'

She turned as if to march off, but he was too quick
for her. His hand reached out for her shoulder and turned
her back to face him. 'I don't think so,' he said gently.

'What did you say?' she breathed.

'I said,' he told her, 'that you are not going to handle
this without my help. I wouldn't stand by and see anyone
forced into marrying someone they obviously loathe.
And I'm certainly not going to let you sign your life
away. I know you, Caron. You may not want to tell me
but you will. Before I'm done you'll tell me everything.'

His thumb brushed her cheek and he added softly,
'And I won't need to use torture to get it out of you.'

'Why should you care?' she said angrily, tears spurting
in her eyes. 'I don't mean anything to you, so just cut
it out.'

He looked at her assessingly and then shrugged. 'I
guess it would be kind of unreasonable for me to expect
you to trust me, considering what you've been going
through—'

'That must be the understatement of the year,' cut in
Caron.

He smiled and carried on. 'But then you have jumped
to quite a few startling conclusions about me.'

Caron clenched her hands. 'I don't care how many
conclusions I've jumped to, but whatever I've told you
about me I would be grateful if you never referred to it
again.'

Colour mounted in her cheeks as he stared at her and
then said slowly, 'I guess you're not going to be feeling
very grateful towards me, then.'

'I don't want to talk about it,' bit out Caron.

'But you will,' replied Ewan gently, reaching for her
hand. 'What kind of supplies did you say you needed?'

'It doesn't matter,' she snapped. 'I suppose I can do without them. But you might as well get this straight. There is no way I am coming out with you and Suzie tonight.'

The bar that Caron had struggled into all those light years ago seemed a different place entirely when she, Ewan and Suzie arrived that evening.

It was packed full of people talking, laughing and drinking, seemingly all at the same time. The band in the corner were playing country music as if their lives depended on it and Caron, who had never much cared for it, suddenly found herself tapping her feet.

'Like it?' asked Ewan, pulling out a chair from a miraculously empty table. Suzie had gone to talk to someone and they were alone.

Caron nodded. On the trip to town that evening she hadn't known whether to be cross with Ewan for the situation he was putting her in or just to pretend that everything was normal. After several minutes of seething frustration she had realised with a jolt that within twenty-four hours she would be saying goodbye to him for ever. Passing everything off with a smile seemed to be by far the easiest course open to her in the meantime.

'It's really lively, isn't it?' she enthused. 'I always thought country music was rather depressing. Like songs about standing by your man even if he was behaving like Attila the Hun.'

'Sounds just up your street,' remarked Ewan, pouring a bottle of beer into her glass.

Someone called him over then and Caron, losing herself in the atmosphere of the place, was suddenly aware that Suzie was sitting next to her.

'Having a nice time?' the girl asked, and Caron nodded, too full of guilt about her feelings for Ewan to trust herself to speak.

'Why did you come all the way out here with that will?' probed Suzie.

Startled, Caron gazed into the other girl's eyes. 'Because it's my job,' she said at last.

'So you wouldn't class yourself as a gold-digger, then?' Suzie pursued.

'Certainly not,' Caron snapped.

'No need to get riled,' remarked Suzie easily. 'But I'd be very careful if I were you. Ewan attracts women like honey traps a bear.'

'Well, if that's the case you seem very philosophical about it all,' grated Caron.

Suzie shrugged and smiled at her. 'One day he'll wake up and realise he's found a woman who's not going to try to use him.'

Caron bit her lip. It was as clear a warning as she'd heard yet. 'You've got nothing to fear from me,' she said in a low voice. 'I'm going back to England tomorrow. In fact I'm getting married on Saturday.'

Suzie looked at her narrowly. 'So you said. But—'

Whatever she had been going to say was cut off by Bill, the cowboy Caron had met at the barbecue the afternoon before, who suddenly came up to Suzie to whisk her away onto the dance floor. 'Sorry, ladies,' he grinned. 'But you'll have to finish your discussion later.'

Caron stood up. It was time for her to go. But when she turned she realised that her path was blocked by Ewan. 'You can't dance on your own,' he told her with a smile.

'I'm going to go,' she said unsteadily.

'I don't think so,' he replied. 'After all, we have so much to talk about.' His hand was on her arm, his body directing her towards the dance floor.

'I'm telling you,' she said furiously, 'I don't want to dance.'

'You remind me of my baby sister throwing her favourite ice cream at me in a fit of temper,' said Ewan evenly, guiding her into the press of people and taking her in his arms.

Caron found herself unthinkingly following his lead. 'It's not exactly disco time at the OK Corral, is it?' she said acidly.

'It's the two-step,' replied Ewan equably. 'And you're supposed to manage it without standing on my feet.'

'Sorry,' she muttered automatically.

He held her closer. 'Just relax, Caron. Everything will be all right.'

And as she swung round in his arms, surrounded by smiling people, it was easy to feel the beginnings of hope. She closed her eyes and let him lead her, refusing to acknowledge the small voice in her head, whispering that she was a fool to even think there might be a way out.

But when the music finished and she opened her eyes to find herself looking clear across the room at Suzie she pulled away from Ewan's arms with a jerk. 'I have to go,' she muttered breathlessly. 'I have to.'

'Escaping again?' he said quietly.

She flushed. 'We have an early start tomorrow, if you're still going to keep your side of the bargain, and I'm feeling rather tired, that's all,' she said stiffly.

Ewan gazed at her shrewdly. 'Oh, I'll keep my side of the bargain,' he replied. 'I wouldn't miss your reunion with Neil even if you offered me my horse's weight in gold.' His eyes twinkled. 'Maybe his weight in platinum, though...'

Caron glared at him. 'Our "reunion" will be probably be taking place at my parents' home in Suffolk. And you will most certainly not be a witness to it.'

Ewan smiled at her. 'But you've invited me to the wedding, sweetheart. How could I possibly refuse to attend?'

Caron glared at him. 'I'm not going to argue the toss with you here and now,' she spat. 'I want to go back to the ranch.'

He shrugged. 'Sure.' Reaching in his pocket, he pulled out a bunch of keys and put them in her hand. 'Take the pick-up.'

She looked at him in astonishment. 'Aren't you going to drive me?'

He smiled down into her eyes. 'No.' He curled her fingers around the correct key and said, 'You're the one who keeps saying what an independent career woman you are. Well, here's your chance. You saw on the way down that it's a real simple route...'

Caron looked at him wordlessly for a few moments and then asked, 'How are you going to get back?'

He shrugged easily. 'I guess Bill will give me and Suzie a lift.'

Caron glared at him. Ewan looked up at the ceiling and then back down at her with that infuriating smile of his. 'And I thought you were quite happy to handle things on your own.'

'I am,' she gritted.

'Strange,' he mused. 'From your reaction I'd say you were getting quite attached to my company.'

'Then you have an even bigger head than I thought,' retorted Caron. 'Please give Suzie my regards, won't you?'

'Is that your best regards,' he asked interestedly, 'or the ones that come with razor blades as optional extras?'

Caron pressed her lips together in silent fury and, turning on her heel, strode out to the pick-up. She drove back in a blazing temper. How dared he treat her so...so...so what?

She eased off the pressure on the accelerator pedal and sighed. She had started out wanting Ewan to treat her like an efficient businesswoman, yet when he did just that she wanted to stamp her foot. And the reason for that, she had to admit, was simply that she was, as he had so rightly guessed, becoming horribly attracted to him.

She had done her best not to give in to these feelings, but it didn't stop the awful rush of guilt she felt about what had happened in the forest every time she saw Suzie.

And the girl's not so coded warning only served to make her feel more disgusted with herself. How could she have let herself get into such a silly, hopeless situation?

She thought of Ewan's deep blue eyes and sighed. How indeed? She strode into the house, straight into her bedroom and tore off her clothes angrily. But once she was in bed her fury dissolved, leaving only an aching void.

She curled up under the sheets, hugging her knees to her chest. After tomorrow she would never see Ewan Cameron again, whatever he said.

She had done the right thing in leaving the bar. She wondered just how much of a hold Suzie had over Ewan, but as the night wore on she realised that in truth the other girl held all the aces. He would be with her now, as he would be in the future, when Caron was no more than a blurred memory.

Restlessly she waited for sleep to erase her thoughts, but she felt ever more awake until, the red figures on her digital alarm clock registering two-thirty, she heard the front door open and Ewan's footsteps.

She listened to him moving about the quiet house, but almost screamed in shock when she heard the knob to her own bedroom door turn.

'You awake, Caron?' he said quietly.

She said nothing, forcing herself to breathe as evenly as she could.

'No one sounds like that when they're really asleep, you know,' he said matter-of-factly.

'Well, I am,' she snapped unthinkingly.

He laughed then, and Caron fought down the impulse to throw her alarm clock at him.

'See you in daylight, Caron,' he chuckled. 'Sleep tight.' And, still laughing, he closed the bedroom door. She heard his footsteps recede and swore under her breath. She was going home not a minute too soon.

CHAPTER SEVEN

CARON'S alarm went off four hours later and blearily she stumbled out of bed. If there was any justice in the world, she thought, Ewan would be feeling even more ghastly than herself.

The sound of singing from the shower made her say something ugly as she pulled her bag onto the bed and began stuffing it with her clothes.

'You may be feeling incredibly cheerful,' she grumbled to him after their scratch breakfast, 'but there's no need to sing about it.'

Ewan smiled at her. 'It's the idea of a short trip to England,' he said. 'Your countryside always looks so beautiful in May.'

Caron stared at him open-mouthed. 'I thought you were joking when you said that last night,' she faltered.

He raised his eyebrows. 'I thought I sounded perfectly serious, myself,' he remarked. 'I was going to discuss it with you more fully when I got back, but when you told me you were asleep it seemed a shame to wake you up.'

'You have no business coming to England,' she said numbly, refusing to rise to his gentle baiting.

'That's where you're wrong,' he contradicted her. 'After all, according to all these papers you so obligingly brought to me, I have quite a bit of property that needs looking at.'

Caron stared at the sheaf of documents he had just picked up. 'Where did you get those?' she demanded.

'From your case yesterday morning,' he said easily. 'After all,' he added silkily, 'it wouldn't have done to drag you away from your beauty sleep.'

'You had no right to rummage through my case,' accused Caron.

Ewan shrugged. 'Quite true. I apologise.'

She glared at him. 'And you don't mean a word of that apology.'

He smiled down into her outraged eyes. 'No, not really. Those papers made very interesting reading.'

Caron gritted her teeth. 'I can't stop you coming to England—'

'No,' he agreed. 'You can't.'

'But if this is just some stupid ploy to wreck my plans you'd better think again. I am going to get married on Saturday, whatever you say.'

He raised an eyebrow. 'Are you always like this in the morning?'

'Don't change the subject,' stormed Caron. 'I—'

He reached for her hand and pulled her to him. 'You what?' he said softly.

'Nothing,' she muttered. 'Nothing.'

He nodded consideringly. 'Come on, then, let's go. We have a plane to catch.'

Caron glared at him. 'Do you know you are probably the most irritating man I have ever met?'

Ewan raised his eyebrows. 'More irritating than your fiancé?'

'Much,' she snapped.

He smiled wickedly at her. 'That's reassuring.'

Outside, she watched him put her bag in the back of the pick-up and then bit her lip as he heaved his own case alongside it.

'This is ridiculous,' she protested. 'You can't possibly come with me.'

He turned and opened the passenger door. With a mock bow he motioned her in. 'Oh, but I'm not coming with you,' he said quietly.

'You aren't?' she faltered, her heart flopping unreasonably.

'No,' he replied. 'On the contrary. It is you who are coming with me.'

Silently she got into the pick-up beside him and watched him drive down to the stables. It was in completely the opposite direction to the road, but it occurred to her that maybe he had some last-minute business.

They parked outside the barn and Ewan got out and went across to talk to one of the hands. She saw him turn back and then stared open-mouthed as he motioned her to get out of the pick-up.

'Come on,' he said, 'You going to sit there all day?'

She got out and watched him take the bags from the back. 'Don't tell me you're planning to go all the way to Calgary on horseback,' she began sarcastically.

He grinned at her. 'Now there's an idea.' And without even realising what she was doing she found herself following him as he walked to the other side of the stables.

'The place is almost deserted at the moment,' he said. 'Most of the boys are out in the pastures, or riding herd on the tourists.'

Caron gazed at a bay mare nuzzling a foal in one of the corrals. 'Do you like them?' he asked quietly.

'They're beautiful,' she breathed, interested in spite of herself.

'I do a bit of breeding,' he acknowledged. 'Quarter horses. You know—the kind you see in a rodeo. They're so intelligent they could probably rope a heifer all by themselves.'

'We don't have many rodeos in England,' said Caron drily.

He looked down at her. 'Maybe you should,' he replied. 'You need a little excitement in your life.'

'Well, you seem to be insisting that I'm going to get jet lag with you,' said Caron as lightly as she could. 'What could possibly be more exciting?'

Ewan stopped and looked down at her. She began to blush furiously under his silent gaze and then turned and walked quickly into the dim interior of the barn. Anywhere to escape those eyes that saw absolutely everything she was thinking.

'Caron,' he said quietly.

She turned, aware of him only as a black silhouette against the blinding sunshine outside.

'What?' she replied, trying hard to cover her flustered nerves and knowing she was failing miserably.

He stepped up to her and dropped the cases on the dusty concrete floor. 'I meant to take you around the outside of the barn,' he said huskily. 'In here a man just can't see straight.'

The blood was hammering through her veins now. 'I'll just—' she began, making as though to push past him, but their hands caught and in a single searing moment she thought her heart had stopped as he stared down at her and then kissed her with a dark intensity that she could not, would not resist.

Everything about him seemed to be as familiar to her as her own body. His clean male smell filled her nostrils and she breathed it in deeply. His fingers took the pins from her hair and as it fell, shining in the gloom, his hands slid under her shirt, moving up her spine as her body arched into his.

Somewhere nearby a horse whickered contentedly, but the noise could have been a crash of thunder and still she and Ewan would not have noticed. He was like a drug she had to have. A drug, a small voice warned, that would ultimately destroy her, if she let him.

'Boss?' A man's voice echoed around the barn. Ewan stilled, and then pulled away, his hand brushing Caron's cheek in one last, lingering caress.

She stood in the semi-darkness, smoothing down her hair as best she could, her hands trembling. She realised that the buttons of her shirt were undone and, suddenly weak as the enormity of what she was doing struck her, she sank to her knees.

'Are you all right?' Ewan squatted down beside her, his hand on her shoulder.

'I think so,' she said shakily. She tried to breathe deeply, tried to regain some shreds of calmness, and then looked at him with a sudden intensity. 'Ewan, we can't do this,' she whispered. 'We can't. Think of Suzie.'

'What about Neil?' he said evenly. 'Aren't you worried about his feelings?'

'He doesn't have any,' she replied bleakly.

'But he does have a mistress and he is blackmailing you,' Ewan remarked.

Caron stood up suddenly, brushing down her jeans. 'Yes, all right. But so what?' she said. 'What do you care? I'm leaving now and I sincerely hope you'll forget the idea of coming to England with me.' She looked at him and bit her lip. 'Go back to Suzie,' she whispered. 'Please, Ewan, I just can't bear this situation.'

'Caron—' he began.

She shook her head fiercely. 'No, Ewan, hear me out. I'm...I'm glad you've got Suzie. Really I am.'

'That's good,' he said noncommittally, sitting on a hay bale and stretching out comfortably.

She glanced sharply at him. She could have sworn he was laughing at her. But his face was wiped clean of any expression. Why did he always manage to move her off balance, even when she knew she was in the right? 'Well, that's all right, then,' she continued uncertainly.

'Nice and neat,' he agreed equably. 'Just the sort of arrangement guaranteed to appeal to a lawyer.'

Caron gritted her teeth. 'Despite the fact that Suzie doesn't like me very much, and I can't blame her for that, I think she's a really nice girl. You're treating us both unreasonably. It's just not fair.'

Her eyes narrowed as she looked down at him, as comfortable as a cat on a cushion, the mocking expression only too clear now in his eyes. 'I just wish you deserved her,' she added pointedly.

Ewan got to his feet and Caron instinctively stepped back, thinking that maybe she shouldn't have been quite so rude.

He dusted off his jeans and then looked thoughtfully at her. 'There's something I have to tell you about Suzie,' he said.

'I told you,' she said coldly, 'I don't want to hear any of your half-baked excuses and explanations. Believe me, I've heard them all before.'

He opened his mouth but Caron instinctively reached out and put her hand on his arm. 'Why can't we be just friends?' she pleaded softly. 'Just for the rest of today? Please humour me, Ewan. Please. I can't deny that whenever you touch me I...'

'You what?' he said quietly.

Caron swallowed. 'Forget it,' she mumbled.

He lifted her face to his. 'I don't think I want to,' he grated. 'What were you going to say?'

She shook herself free of him. 'It wasn't important,' she forced out. 'I was just being silly.' She tried to look at him squarely and found herself unable to.

'Very silly,' she added, unable to hide the quaver in her voice. 'It's just that this whole situation is impossible, Ewan. I'm going back to England and I'm going to marry Neil.'

His eyebrows met in one angry line and she stepped back involuntarily. 'And whatever you may think,' she added recklessly, 'I really do love him very much.'

'Then you must be a sucker for punishment,' said Ewan drily. 'You haven't even reached the altar yet and you're already prepared to put up with being cheated on and blackmailed.'

Caron licked dry lips. 'That was an exaggeration,' she whispered. 'I was just being over-emotional.' Anger flared within her as she saw the cynical twist of his lips. 'For goodness' sake,' she burst out, 'I'm getting married at the weekend. I'm just a bundle of nerves. Neil and I had a silly row and that's all there is to it. Believe me.'

He shook his head. 'You're wasted being a lawyer, you know,' he said, closing the gap between them once more.

'Well, housekeeping doesn't pay as much,' she flashed.

'Oh, I wasn't thinking of your housekeeping skills,' he murmured. 'With talent like yours you should be on the stage.'

'That's a rotten thing to say,' she forced out. She turned on her heel, choking back desperate tears, but Ewan was too quick for her. He pulled her round to face him, his hands grasping her arms.

'Let me go,' she begged.

'Where to?' he said roughly, shaking her. 'Your own private purgatory?'

She gazed at him as steadily as she could. 'I'm getting married on Saturday,' she said in a low voice. 'I've fulfilled my part of the deal, Ewan. I've done your housekeeping. All you have to do is take me to the airport and wave me off.' She looked at him and then added with sudden uncertainty, 'Please.'

His hands dropped and, as he stared at her, the realisation that she might never see this man again hit her with full force. Tears welling in her eyes, she reached blindly for his hand. 'This is going to be our last day together and I'd like something happy to remember,' she pleaded.

'Don't look at me that way you do sometimes and make me feel guilty about Suzie, or cross-question me about Neil. Please. I can't explain. Don't make me. But you seem to be the only friend I've got at the moment. And God knows I need one.'

He looked down at her steadily and then tipped up her chin once more. But, instead of subjecting her to that blue-eyed stare that seemed to turn her inside out so easily, he kissed her lightly on the lips. 'You can't expect to be friends with someone that you continually lie to, Caron.'

She searched his face, but his expression was closed in, distant. 'Can't you even trust me?' she asked uncertainly.

He laughed shortly. 'Do *you* trust *me*?' he said.

She thought of Suzie and swallowed. 'I don't know,' she muttered. 'But I feel like I ought to. I just don't know enough about you.'

He stared down at her for a long moment and then, sighing, tugged a stray lock of her hair. 'Glad to see we have something in common, at least.'

He bent to pick up their bags and walked to the doorway at the opposite end of the barn, Caron following as though her feet had suddenly become encased in lead.

They emerged blinking in the sunshine, and she gazed speechlessly at a helicopter parked at the far end of the yard, behind a belt of trees.

'You must have some very rich clients,' she said at last. 'Don't tell me you're teaching some sheikh how to rope a heifer?'

Ewan smiled grimly at her as they neared the big, shining machine. 'That's two things those men don't need,' he replied. 'Money and riding lessons. I reckon some of them were born on a horse.'

Caron looked at him, puzzled. 'You sound as though you know quite a lot about them.'

'I've visited a few,' he replied equably. 'On business.'

Caron's jaw dropped. But before she could say anything he held open the door of the helicopter and turned to her where she was still standing in the hot sunshine. 'You going to stay there all day or are you going to get in?'

Silently she watched him make the pre-flight checks and then settle himself behind the controls. Equally silently she put on her headset when he put his on and motioned her to do the same.

Within a few minutes they were pulling away from the ground and soaring into the blue, blue sky.

Ewan was silent for a moment as he listened to last-minute instructions from Control, and then looked at her and smiled once more, the grim lines in his face suddenly softening.

'This could take us straight to Calgary,' he said, 'but then we'd have several hours to wait for our flight, so I thought we might as well do a little sightseeing on the way. There is nothing in the world like these mountains.'

'Besides,' he shrugged, 'I want to talk to you without the slightest risk of being interrupted by wranglers who suddenly seem to have lost their initiative or Suzie boring me to death about her important appointments and lack of transport.'

Caron turned on him furiously. 'How dare you talk like that about her?'

Ewan shrugged. 'It's not difficult. She's my sister.'

Caron's mouth sagged open. 'Your sister?' she whispered. 'Why didn't you tell me?'

Ewan looked sideways at her. 'Because you had decided to believe otherwise. You told me you didn't want to hear any excuses or explanations—remember?'

Caron looked out of the clear Perspex nose of the helicopter and said nothing. What had Ewan told her? That she jumped to so many conclusions she should enter the Olympics. And he had been right.

He threaded the machine expertly through the snowy mountain peaks, jagged edges of ice and rock reaching up all around them.

'What's that furry green stuff that looks like grass?' asked Caron, too proud to ask the thousand other more important questions that were clamouring in her mind.

'Pine trees,' said Ewan. 'Want a close-up?' And, turning, they skimmed low over the tops. Then the trees cleared and Caron could see a beautiful mountain meadow below them.

With a jolt she realised that they were landing. 'Why are we stopping?' she forced out.

The craft bumped gently on the sun-washed mountain grass and the rotors whined to a halt. 'As I said,' Ewan told her, 'we need to talk.'

Caron stared into eyes as blue as the sky above and swallowed. 'Don't tell me,' she began. 'In the first place you are not a poor cowboy. Correct?'

Ewan nodded. She reddened and ploughed on. 'In fact you're probably some rich businessman who's quite at home doing deals in the Middle East. Right?'

Ewan shrugged. 'Not quite,' he said. 'But near enough. Go on.'

Caron swallowed again. 'And Suzie is not your girlfriend but your sister,' she added in a low voice.

He smiled at her. 'Yes,' he agreed. 'In fact, those are her jeans that you're wearing.'

Caron had a sudden memory of Ewan handing them to her after her first shower. 'But she told me she loved you,' she said unthinkingly. 'I thought she was trying to warn me off.'

'Maybe she was,' he replied. 'My last girlfriend turned out to be more interested in my bank balance than in me as a person. She and Suzie did not hit it off, to say the least.'

'I can't imagine you being fooled by a gold-digger,' remarked Caron.

'Oh, I knew what she was after,' replied Ewan easily. 'But she was good fun, and quite open in her admiration of my money. Ultimately she just bored the pants off me, and when I lost interest she became rather vindictive. Especially towards Suzie.'

Caron stared at him speechlessly. 'You can really be quite cruel, can't you?'

He shook his head. 'She knew the score, Caron. I was quite prepared to be generous, but she just wanted to move the goalposts.'

'You mean she fell for you,' Caron whispered.

He shrugged. 'She fell for what I represented, not for what I am. In any case, I didn't go to all the trouble of bringing you out here to discuss my love life.'

'Well, we're not going to discuss mine,' she responded tartly.

He suppressed a smile. 'We could talk about your wonderful ability for summing people up.'

'You didn't help,' she flashed. 'You went out of your way to let me think Suzie was your girlfriend.'

'Jealousy is a wonderful thing, isn't it?' he said softly. 'It brings all sorts of other emotions so quickly to the surface.'

'I was not jealous,' snapped Caron. 'I had other things on my mind. In any case,' she added, 'I just wasn't thinking straight when I jumped to those conclusions.'

Ewan squeezed her hand. 'How I envy you your female intuition.'

'Oh, shut up,' she muttered furiously. 'It's obvious that every time I've opened my mouth since I arrived I've put my foot right in it. Haven't I?'

'Well, I wouldn't go that far,' Ewan began. 'But—' He stopped. 'What's the matter?' he said. 'Is there a bear behind me or something?'

'No,' retorted Caron. 'It's just that there's a snake in front of me—you.'

Ewan stretched out comfortably on the grass. 'Is that another conclusion you're jumping to?'

Caron stood up abruptly. 'You must be the most arrogant man I've ever met,' she grated. 'I hate the way you've gone out of your way to pull the wool over my eyes ever since I got here.'

He lifted an eyebrow. 'Gone out of my way?'

'All right.' She blushed hotly. 'I might have jumped to a few conclusions. But you didn't exactly put me in the picture. You let me just bumble on, making a complete fool of myself. I bet you were laughing yourself sick. Is that how you get your kicks?'

He reached out and grasped her ankle. 'I'm quite prepared to show you how I get my kicks,' he said silkily.

'Don't you dare,' she said furiously, lashing out with her free foot and falling on top of him.

'Well, this will do for a start,' he replied, laughing into her flushed face. She looked long into his eyes and then lay quietly in his arms.

'It still doesn't really change anything,' she said quietly.

'What doesn't?'

'Suzie being your sister,' she forced out. 'Even if you had been straight with me right from the beginning it wouldn't have made any difference. I've still got to go home. As far as Neil is concerned there is no way out.'

He kissed her hair. 'There's always a way out.' His heartbeat was deep and steady and Caron felt a thrill of unreasonable hope. Slowly she reached up, her fingertips caressing his ear, his hair, the silky strength of his neck. His fingers reached around her wrist and brought it to his lips.

'Tell me who you really are,' she whispered. 'Just so that I don't jump to any more conclusions.'

He kissed her hand. 'I grew up in that ranch house that you have been so assiduously cleaning,' he began.

'But my father wasn't as good with money as he was with horses.

'He borrowed a bit more money than he should have done, and when I was a teenager the banks foreclosed. The ranch was sold out from under our feet and we went to live in Calgary.'

Ewan shifted Caron onto the grass and rolled over on his side to face her. 'My father died a few years later. I reckon that being bankrupted just about killed him, and living in a city did the rest.'

'What did you do?' she breathed.

Ewan shrugged. 'Went to work. This part of Canada is a lot like Texas—full of oil and cattle. I went to night school and I got into oil. Made a lot of money, I have to admit.'

'That's why you've been to the Middle East,' said Caron.

He nodded. 'Yes. Not to do any deals, really. But it's a good idea to see how the other half lives, so to speak.' He looked up at the sky. 'I was doing real well for myself at that point and I remember talking to this fabulously wealthy sheikh. You know what was the most important thing to him?'

Caron shook her head soundlessly and Ewan grinned. 'His falcons, his horses and his wives. In that order.'

She glared at him. 'So you came home and put in an order for all three.'

'Oh, I think he had more than three wives,' said Ewan, deliberately misunderstanding her. 'But I took his point. And when I got home I bought the ranch my family had been evicted from. When I looked out of the window at those mountains I knew I was on the right road.'

He turned over onto his stomach, picked a long piece of grass and began to chew it. 'I come here most summers now. It's a working ranch, not a rich man's toy. We have near on two hundred and thirty head of horses here and the ranch caters for tourists who want to ride the trail in the Rockies.'

'What happens in the winter?' asked Caron. 'You can't ride a trail if it's six feet deep in snow.'

He smiled at her. 'When autumn sets in the horses get taken back to another ranch I have near Calgary. It takes two weeks and it's the hardest work I've ever known. No wonder the boys made such a mess of the kitchen when they brought them out.'

'Humph,' snorted Caron. 'Knowing the mess it was in, I wouldn't be at all surprised if they gave the horses bed and breakfast in your house.'

Ewan smiled at her. 'No. It would have been a lot tidier if they'd done that. My horses have high standards.'

'There's one thing I don't understand,' said Caron after a few moments. 'If you have a lot of business interests, how come you can just drop them for the summer? You have to keep in touch, surely?'

Ewan threw the grass away and looked up at the sky. 'If you were going to be my housekeeper for much longer you'd have realised when you got to my study that I can still keep tabs on all my other business from there. It has a fax and a computer with a phone link—everything I need to keep in touch. I have the helicopter too, if I need to get anywhere fast.

'I fixed it all up when I moved in, because I was afraid I'd get bored out in the middle of nowhere. I'd forgotten, you see, just how much I loved this part of the country.

'I thought it was just going to be a regular break from business, but the more I come here, the more I want to wind down on that sort of thing and just concentrate on breeding horses and looking at the mountains.'

Caron got up quietly and walked away, deep in thought, then stopped abruptly, staring unseeingly at the patch of grass at her feet. The light touch of his hand on her shoulder almost made her jump out of her skin.

'Caron?'

She turned to face him, as jerky as a clockwork doll. 'It's no good, Ewan. I have to go back to him. I have to.'

He nodded slowly. 'I know.'

She smiled doubtfully at his apparent calmness. 'I'm glad that's all clear, then.'

Then she noticed a harsh light in Ewan's eyes that she hadn't bargained on. She shivered involuntarily. But what could she say to him? Nothing, she told herself firmly. Absolutely nothing.

'I am going to marry him,' she repeated uncertainly, more to herself than to Ewan.

His eyes narrowed. 'Maybe,' he said grimly. 'And if you do how long do you think it will be before you begin spending all your evenings on your own, while Neil is happily tucked up with his mistress?'

She turned away, choking back desperate tears, but Ewan reached out and pulled her to him, her body refusing to resist.

'Please don't, Ewan,' she pleaded, swallowing hard. 'Just take me to the airport and—'

'And what?' he demanded.

She swallowed. 'And let's just forget everything that has happened.'

His fingers cupped her chin. 'It's not what has happened, Caron, that's bothering me. It's what might happen.'

She smiled weakly at him. 'Oh, the usual thing, probably—a quick affair, followed by bitterness and bad memories.'

He gazed deep into her eyes. 'Usual, huh? Is that the usual thing with you?'

Her fingers slid around his wrist; his pulse was slow and steady. 'No,' she said steadily. 'But I thought it would be with you.'

He looked at her for a long moment and then dropped his hand. 'Maybe you're right.' His eyes glinted. 'So, I accept.'

'Accept?' she faltered. 'Accept what?'

'The invitation to your wedding, of course,' Ewan drawled.

She stared at him for a long moment and then pulled away from him, her eyes blazing. 'You have got to be joking! I know you said you were coming with me, but you can't possibly—'

'Why not?' he shrugged. 'If I want to come to England there's not much you can do about it, is there now?'

She compressed her lips. 'No.'

'Well,' he resumed more gently, 'you can either pretend you don't know me or you can talk to me. It's up to you.'

'Nothing that concerns you is ever up to me,' flashed Caron. 'You just spend your entire time winding me up in knots and then telling me it's all my fault.'

He smiled at her and put his hands up. 'Guilty as charged, your Honour.'

She looked at him and said nothing. He dropped his hands and added, 'I must say, I'm looking forward to meeting Neil.'

Caron shook her head violently as she realised just how much in deadly earnest he was. 'No,' she gasped. 'You can't.'

His being in England was risky enough. The idea of him meeting Neil was just too dangerous to contemplate. It could mean disaster for all her carefully laid plans. His eyes missed nothing, and he was afraid of nothing. She simply couldn't allow him to wreck everything.

He was looking at her now with those intense blue eyes and she realised she had spoken too vehemently. She licked dry lips and then whispered, 'You really don't have to come all the way to England with me. It's a silly idea.'

'Oh, but I do,' he contradicted her, with a slow smile. 'After all, I'm a man of property now.'

'What property?' asked Caron, suddenly wary of the mischief in his eyes.

Ewan took a folded paper from his pocket and smoothed it out. 'According to those documents you so obligingly brought me, it seems I am now the proud owner of a manor house somewhere in deepest Suffolk.'

'Give me that,' she said hoarsely.

He looked at her and raised an eyebrow. 'Such manners,' he drawled.

She glared at him. 'Damn you and your manners, Ewan Cameron. Let me see that paper.'

He held it out to her with a sardonic smile and she scanned it swiftly, her lips parting in astonishment. 'But that's my village,' she whispered at last. 'You've inherited Sir William's property. He was my father's closest friend. I don't...'

'Well,' said Ewan. 'He was my mother's cousin too.'

'But you can't...' Caron gasped.

Ewan took the papers gently from her grasp. 'Oh, but I can,' he said gently. 'And just think—we'll be neighbours.'

Caron swallowed. 'You'll hate it,' she said. 'There are no mountains to speak of in Suffolk. Let me go back and sell it for you. You would get an excellent price. Enough to buy hundreds of horses—'

'Caron,' he interrupted her gently, 'I already have hundreds of horses.'

She almost stamped her foot in frustration. 'Why can't you just accept that I don't want you to come to my wedding?'

He shook his head. 'Oh, I can accept that,' he said quietly. 'But there's just one thing.'

'What?' she asked unthinkingly.

He gazed at her steadily. 'There's not going to be any wedding.'

CHAPTER EIGHT

'I MUST say, your Mr Cameron seems a very nice man,' remarked Caron's mother, before adding helpfully, 'Lift your arms higher, dear.'

Caron reached up obediently as the dressmaker, her mouth full of pins, made last-minute alterations to her wedding dress. It was two days since they had arrived back in England and Ewan, after seeing her to her home and briefly meeting her parents, had simply seemed to vanish.

'He's not *my* Mr Cameron, Mother,' she said tartly, reddening helplessly under the scrutiny of the elegant figure sitting in the corner of the salon. 'He's a business acquaintance, that's all.'

'Really?' said her mother. 'Well, your father liked him on sight, so we've invited him to dinner tomorrow evening.'

Caron dropped her arms in shock, pins sticking in her from all directions. 'You've what?'

'Well, since he's inherited the manor house, it seemed the right thing to do, especially since your father and Sir William were such close friends, so I rang him this morning.'

'He was in?' breathed Caron. 'But I thought—'

Mrs Lane nodded. 'He does seem to have a lot of business to see to in London, but he said he would love to come.' She smiled. 'He has such a lovely voice, a sort of soft drawl, and such exquisite manners. Really, dear,

135

why you couldn't have fallen for someone like him instead of Neil, who—'

'That's enough, Mother,' snapped Caron. 'Neil is the man I'm marrying and you might as well get used to the fact.'

Her mother stood up and kissed her daughter on the cheek. 'Darling, you know we'll stand by you, whatever you want. It just seems . . .' She shrugged.

Caron stared into Mrs Lane's eyes. 'Just what?'

'Well,' her mother continued with searing shrewdness, 'I sometimes think that it is you who has not quite got used to the idea of this marriage. It all seems so sudden. Neil never appears to even want to take you out much. And that last-minute business trip you made...' She lifted her hands in the air.

Caron shrugged off the foaming yards of Belgian lace and, grabbing her jeans, turned to look pleadingly at her mother. 'Maybe it's not conventional,' she said. 'But, believe me, I really do know what I'm doing. Really.'

Her mother looked at her watch. 'Well, I expect it's just nerves all round. But I must admit I'll be happier when we get tonight's rehearsal over.'

'Rehearsal?' asked Caron blankly.

'For your wedding, dear,' her mother replied patiently. 'Remember we had to postpone it because of your trip? Really, ever since you came back from Canada with Ewan Cameron your mind has been like a sieve.'

The village church seemed cold in the evening light, and Caron shivered. Would she really be doing all this for real on Saturday? She glanced around the pews and stiffened. There was a dark figure sitting at the back that she had not bargained on being there at all.

Leaving the vicar to fuss round the exact positions of Neil and his best man, she hurried down the aisle. 'What are you doing here?' she whispered fiercely.

Ewan leaned back in the pew and smiled at her. 'Taking in the local scenery, what else?'

'This is my wedding rehearsal,' she snapped.

He nodded. 'So I see. Which one is Neil? The one with the superior expression, or the one with spots?'

'The one with—' she began unthinkingly, before realising how close she had come to falling into his simple trap. She clenched her teeth. This man was the absolute limit.

Ewan shook his head, his eyes glittering with amusement. 'Really, Caron, I despair.'

'Good,' she said coldly. 'At last you're doing something I approve of.'

'Unlike you,' he murmured.

'I'm going through with this wedding,' she said defiantly.

'Yes,' Ewan nodded. 'So you keep saying.' He smiled. 'You going to be dressed like that?'

She could feel her throat constricting at the look in his eyes and shook her head quickly. 'I have a dress,' she forced out.

He stood up abruptly. 'Well, I can't stand here all night and talk fashion with you, much as you know I'd like to.'

'Where are you going?' she asked impulsively.

He gazed at her steadily, his expression unreadable. 'To renew old acquaintances, I guess you could say, Caron.'

'Who?' she challenged. 'Who are you going to see?' The words were out before she could stop them and in the silence that followed she bit her lip. 'Sorry. I don't mean to pry.'

He reached out and tugged a strand of her hair. 'If you really want to know,' he said softly, 'I've just met a wonderful woman who works in the civil service.'

Caron's heart plummeted. 'That was quick,' she choked out.

'Amazing what you can do when you try,' he agreed.

She backed away from him. 'I've got to go.'

He nodded. 'See you at dinner tomorrow. Good luck with the rehearsal.' His lips twisted as he added, 'Or should that be break a leg?'

The doorbell shrilled as though someone was leaning on it, and Caron swore under her breath as she ran down the stairs, trying helplessly to do her zip up at the same time. Where had the housekeeper, Mrs Peabody, got to?

She held her dress with one hand as she turned the catch and then gasped in astonishment as she saw Ewan standing on the step.

Gone was the cowboy she had cooked and cleaned for. In his place stood a man in a beautifully cut dark dinner suit. 'Will I do?' he asked sardonically.

'You forgot your stetson,' she mumbled. 'And your cowboy boots.'

'You'll be telling me next I should have packed a six-shooter,' he replied equably, stepping over the threshold.

'Maybe you should have done,' she said mutinously. 'Then I could have got you arrested for terrorism at the airport.'

He smothered a smile. 'You mean after I told everybody we were a honeymoon couple?'

'Especially after that,' Caron retorted. 'I've never felt so embarrassed in all my life. Especially when that nice old man sitting across the aisle bought us champagne.'

'Maybe he'll buy us some more on the journey back,' mused Ewan.

'Don't count on it,' snapped Caron.

'And I thought brides were supposed to be radiant with happiness,' he replied. 'Another illusion shattered.'

'I might be radiant if you weren't here,' she retorted, her hand still on the door. 'Why don't you go home and tame a bear or something?'

'Oh, I don't know,' he said softly. 'There's always something to tame, wherever you go. And certain things are much more of a challenge than an old bear.'

The colour mounted in her cheeks as his eyes travelled down the clinging sparkly material of her dress and then back to her face. 'Very nice,' he said at last. 'But it seems a bit on the loose side.'

'If you hadn't hammered our doorbell so insistently,' she snapped, 'I would have been able to do my zip up before I got down the stairs.'

Ewan reached over her shoulder and closed the door. 'Allow me,' he said quietly, turning her around and fastening her dress with swift efficiency.

She turned to face him rather breathlessly. 'You didn't have to come, you know,' she whispered fiercely.

He raised an eyebrow. 'Your mother invited me.'

She clenched her jaw. 'It would have been better if you had refused.'

'Better for whom?' he said lightly, his finger stroking her cheek and then dropping to her throat. 'Better for you, or better for me? Or, perhaps, better for Neil?'

'I'm getting married tomorrow afternoon,' she gasped. 'How can you torture me like this?'

'As easily as I seem to be torturing myself,' he replied grimly. 'And don't you think you should show me in? Or are we eating off the hall-stand tonight?'

Caron led him across the hall to the sitting-room door, but paused for a moment before pushing it open. 'What's the matter?' murmured Ewan. 'Afraid I'll say something I shouldn't?'

She looked at him in horror. 'You wouldn't dare!' she said.

'Don't bank on it,' he replied easily.

She swallowed desperately. 'Ewan, please—' she began, and then stopped.

He looked at her questioningly. 'Is Neil in there?'

She nodded. 'Yes, with my mother and father.' Her fingers were on the doorknob, but his hand closed over them, his other cupping her jaw. 'Ewan, this is madness,' she breathed.

'Yes,' he whispered, his lips on hers, his body pushing hers against the old oak door.

She thought for one horrified instant of what would happen if the door gave way and they fell into the room, right at the feet of Neil and her parents.

Or, even more likely, what would happen if somebody inside the room were simply to open the door? Her hand pushed hard against Ewan's chest. But it was like pushing the Rockies themselves and then, as his hands moved up her spine and began unzipping the dress he had only minutes ago fastened, all sense of time and place seemed to simply dissolve and she found herself responding to him with the same passionate intensity.

Hungrily she reached for him; his hands were at the base of her spine, moulding her body into his. 'Ewan, I...' But her voice died as he pushed the straps of her dress from her shoulders, his hands cupping her breasts, his fingers fluttering over their hardening nipples.

She knew that her dress was falling to the floor, but as his tongue tasted the sweet moisture of her mouth, demanding, claiming, possessing, she suddenly did not care what was going to happen next.

Was it seconds or hours later that he stopped and pulled away? 'Very much still the chaste bride, I see,' he said softly, taking in her flushed face and glittering eyes.

Caron stared at him, the colour draining from her features as she took in his harsh words. 'So that was just some sort of test,' she whispered.

'Oh, don't worry,' he grated. 'You still get top marks.'

'How dare you do that to me?' she gasped.

He shrugged. 'In this world I've found I can always take what I want.'

'Not me,' she flared. 'I've told you a thousand times, Ewan Cameron. No matter what you do, I'm getting married to another man. So you'd better get used to it.'

'What does that make this, then?' he enquired grimly, his eyes moving once more over every inch of her body. 'Useful practice for tomorrow night?'

'Don't you dare look at me like that!' she spat.

'Why not?' he grated. 'You're a beautiful woman, Caron. It's difficult not to stare, seeing as how I've just taken most of your clothes off.'

She glared at him. 'You are despicable,' she stormed. 'Do you know that?'

'Sure I do,' he replied, bending down to help her pick up her dress. 'It seems to be your word of the month. Besides,' he shrugged, 'despicable is my middle name.'

She eased the straps back over her shoulders and stared at him breathlessly. 'You shouldn't have come here, Ewan.'

He smiled at her, turning her round once more so that he could do her zip up. 'Well, now I'm here, perhaps I can offer you some useful advice.'

'I doubt it,' she snapped, and then, as his features softened in amusement, she faltered. 'All right, what?' she asked, watching his hand begin to turn the doorknob.

'Your lipstick's smudged.' And, with one final challenging look, he pushed open the door and entered the room.

With a strangled sob she fled to the hall mirror and scrubbed her lips savagely with a tissue. She had expected the damage to her make-up to be much greater, as if Ewan's kiss had somehow implanted a big neon sign on her forehead, flashing on and off with the word GUILTY, GUILTY, GUILTY.

But instead the face that stared back from the mirror was just the same as always. A little flushed, perhaps, highlighting the dark circles under her eyes that now seemed to be a permanent feature. She smoothed her hands nervously down her dress and then, turning, followed where Ewan had entered.

She had walked only two steps into the room when she realised that there was another woman there, apart from her mother. And it was the last woman on earth she would have expected to see: Kate Andrews, Neil's mistress.

'I didn't realise you were planning on doing any business tonight,' she said as lightly as she could to Neil. It was strange, but she had always thought of him as classically handsome. He was tall, blond and blue-eyed, and turned most women's heads, but in the same room as Ewan he looked as alive as a marble statue.

'I'm not, *darling*,' Neil said gravely, emphasising the last word and looking across at Ewan. 'Your mother asked me to bring someone along to make up the numbers. And Kate very kindly agreed.'

He handed her a drink. 'After all, we wouldn't want Mr Cameron to feel left out, would we?'

Caron followed his gaze and gripped the stem of her sherry glass more and more tightly as she saw Kate smile up into Ewan's eyes and then lay a hand on his arm.

'Fast worker, your Mr Cameron,' murmured Neil, a pulse hammering in his cheek.

'He's not *my* Mr Cameron,' snarled Caron, the glass suddenly shattering in her fingers.

She stared unseeingly at her hand as a thin swirl of blood welled up in her palm. And then, with a gasp, she ran out of the room.

'It doesn't say much for the future of your marriage if you can't even stand to be in the same room as your prospective husband,' came a voice she knew only too well.

Caron, bathing her hand under the cold tap in the downstairs loo, whirled round and found herself almost in Ewan's arms.

'This room's too small,' she said breathlessly, fighting down the temptation to throw her arms around him.

'Really?' he said, backing her up against the sink. 'I would have thought it was just the right size.'

Caron gazed at him and then, putting her hand behind her for some support, yelped as the shards of glass dug deeper into her flesh.

'Let me look at that,' he demanded.

Falteringly she put her hand out. 'It's nothing really,' she said shakily.

'Well, it won't kill you,' he agreed, 'but you need to get that glass out.' Lifting her hand under the light, he took a penknife from his pocket and extracted a tiny pair of tweezers from it. 'This might hurt,' he said softly, intent on his task.

A few minutes later he looked her full in the face and, his arms sliding round her, kissed her lightly on the lips.

'You didn't need to do that,' she said raggedly.

'On the contrary,' he told her. 'I always like to kiss things better.'

She swallowed. 'Ewan, they'll be wondering where we are.'

He shook his head. 'No, they won't. I told them.'

'You told them?' she repeated shakily.

'Of course,' he nodded. 'Even Neil agreed that since I said I was good at first aid I would be the best person to go after you—although I have a feeling that that was more because he's jealous of the way I'm paying attention to Kate than because of any feelings of deep sympathy for you.'

'What attention to Kate?' she demanded, suddenly flooded with jealousy.

His lips quirked into a smile. 'Oh, the usual things that a man says softly to an attractive woman,' he said. 'If I'm very lucky Neil might completely lose his cool, and then I will have a very good excuse to throw him through the nearest window. Although—what the hell?— I might just do it anyway, reason or no reason.'

A sudden picture of Kate's smiling face made Caron push hard against him. 'What might work in a saloon bar in the Rockies isn't necessarily the done thing in Suffolk, you know,' she retorted.

His smile broadened and he stepped back, motioning for her to go first. 'Thanks for the advice,' he drawled. 'But you should know by now that I've never cared very much for "the done thing".'

She stopped in the hall and stared at him. 'Where have you been the last few days, anyway?' she demanded.

He lifted an eyebrow. 'And I thought it was you who didn't want to see me.'

'If I thought you were keeping out of my way, simply to spare my feelings,' she retorted, 'I'd be amazed.'

'So would I,' he agreed simply. 'And I'm sorry to disappoint you, but I've had some rather pressing engagements in London.'

'Who with?' Caron said hotly. 'That woman in the civil service you mentioned?' She stopped. 'I'm sorry,' she forced out. 'That was awful of me. I guess it's just nerves. I have no right to pry into your affairs.'

He looked at her assessingly. 'No, in the circumstances I guess you haven't.' And, turning, he led the way into the dining room.

They were all sitting down as she walked in behind him, her head held high, her hand wrapped in a handkerchief. Her heart thudded as she realised that the only two vacant spaces left were next to each other.

Neil, busy in conversation with Mr Lane, did not look up as she came in, nor when Ewan pulled out her chair, waiting for her to sit down.

But the seemingly trivial action caught the attention of the rest of the room. To Caron it was as though someone had taken a snapshot of the moment. Her mother's expression was one of pleasure at simple good manners, her father's one of astonishment; Kate merely afforded her a sour glance, while Neil, busy explaining some new deal to Caron's father, only stopped talking

when he realised that his prospective father-in-law was
staring over his shoulder.

Then Neil too turned round, staring for the first time
deep into Caron's eyes, and he read what was written in
her heart.

'Caron?' prompted Ewan gently.

Swiftly she made for the chair. 'Thanks,' she muttered
as he pushed her in, not daring to catch his eye.

'No trouble,' he replied easily, resuming both his seat
and his conversation with Kate as though nothing had
happened.

But something had happened, and they both knew it.

Caron ate mechanically, not noticing what was put in
front of her, every nerve stretched to concentrate on
Ewan. He wouldn't really carry out his threat and say
something embarrassing, would he? And who exactly
was this mystery female civil servant he was meeting?

And then, as she realised how well he and Kate seemed
to be getting on, she thought with a pang how stupidly
naïve she had been. Ewan had accepted that she was
getting married, and was merely giving way to his
predatory instincts.

She smiled bitterly to herself; she had been so right,
that day back in the forest. And she had been a fool not
to listen more closely to her intuition.

The meal over, her father got up and left the room,
only to return shortly cradling two bottles of champagne. 'Couldn't really ask Mrs Peabody to get them,'
he explained to the room in general. 'She's not too steady
on her pins these days.'

'I really think you're being too kind to that housekeeper of yours,' said Neil. 'She's incredibly inefficient.
You should let her go.'

'You mean sack her,' Caron flashed. 'But she's been with us for years. It would be awful to treat her like that.'

Neil ignored her, smiling instead at Ewan. 'I bet you wouldn't be so squeamish, Mr Cameron. What would you do if your housekeeper didn't come up to scratch?'

Caron could hear her heartbeat thundering in her ears. Why did Neil have to be so ignorantly bang on target?

Ewan looked at him steadily. 'My last housekeeper was so awful, I threw her in the horse trough,' he said mildly. 'But I reckon Mrs Peabody and I could get along just fine.'

'Horse trough?' repeated Neil incredulously. 'That was pretty extreme, wasn't it?'

Caron clenched her fingers so tightly that her knuckles stood out whitely.

'You were there at the time, I seem to remember,' said Ewan, turning to her with that unmistakable glint in his eye. 'Did you think it was extreme?'

She shook her head. 'No,' she forced out at last. 'It wasn't extreme—coming from an employer who's a cross between Genghis Khan and Attila the Hun.'

'Caron!' breathed her mother.

Ewan's lips curved into a smile. 'Well, I certainly do seem to be going up in your estimation, don't I?'

Caron opened her mouth, but her father broke in before she could get a word out. 'I think we'd better open the champagne,' he said hurriedly.

The pale gold liquid bubbled up in the crystal flutes. Her father stood up and beamed at his guests. 'Well, as we all know, Caron and Neil are getting married tomorrow afternoon, and I should just like to propose a toast to their future happiness.' He lifted his glass and repeated, 'Caron and Neil.'

His wife lifted her glass too and after a moment's hesitation Kate also raised hers. They looked expectantly at Ewan.

'Well?' said Caron, following their gaze and forcing herself to sound calm. 'Aren't you going to wish me luck?'

He stared into the depths of his glass and then raised it to her. 'To the man who has your heart in his keeping. May he never let it go.'

'I don't know why you just didn't get out a gauntlet and whack Neil across the face with it,' Caron accused Ewan in an undertone as they sipped coffee later in the sitting room.

'Your mother said black tie,' replied Ewan equably. 'She didn't mention anything about gauntlets. Besides,' he shrugged, 'I'm fresh out of them.'

'More coffee, Mr Cameron?' said her mother as she sat down beside them, and the retort Caron was going to make died on her lips.

He smiled at her mother. It was, Caron noticed, one of his four-star heart-stoppers. 'Call me Ewan, Mrs Lane. We're neighbours after all.'

Caron gritted her teeth and turned to her mother. 'Mr Cameron was just telling me that he has to go home on urgent business. Isn't that a shame?' she lied brightly.

Her mother's face fell. But before she could speak Neil was in front of Caron, his hand grasping her cut palm painfully hard. 'Really, darling,' he said in mock exasperation, 'you must stop monopolising our guest. I know your mother is dying to talk to him, and I'd quite like to monopolise you myself.'

Caron had the sudden impression of Ewan like a live bomb waiting to go off. She shivered involuntarily, and then her resolve hardened as she thought of how he had treated her in the hall. She would marry Neil, and it would serve Ewan damn well right, she thought with sudden fury. He simply shouldn't have come.

With one final, painful tug on her hand Neil pulled her up, the epitome of the loving bridegroom. 'Of course, darling,' Caron beamed at him. 'Let's go into the garden, shall we? The roses are beautiful in the moonlight.'

And, leading a suddenly bemused Neil away, she flung open the French windows and stepped into the cool night air.

'What the hell is that man doing here?' he demanded, when they were far enough away from the house not to be overheard.

Caron gazed at him in astonishment. 'What do you care?' she said.

Neil stepped towards her. 'I care,' he said slowly, as if speaking to a stupid child, 'because this wedding is going ahead, come hell or high water. I haven't come this far to see my plans in ruins now.'

'Why should Ewan ruin your plans?' enquired Caron as steadily as she could.

'Don't you know anything about him?' demanded Neil.

'He's a pretty good horseman,' said Caron, suddenly smiling to herself.

'He's pretty famous in certain circles as a ruthless businessman,' snarled Neil. 'What did you tell him?'

'It's none of your business what I told Ewan,' she blazed. 'I've agreed to marry you, haven't I? And I came back, didn't I? What's any of this got to do with Ewan?'

Neil opened his mouth and then closed it again. Eyeing Caron warily, he said, 'Ewan's behaviour with Kate this

evening has been disgustingly over the top. I really
thought at one point he was going to kiss her hand.'

Caron suddenly snapped back to the present, a little
of Neil's bitterness entering her own heart. 'Well, that's
your problem, isn't it?' she said as sweetly as she could.
'After all, I'm hardly going to object if someone can
find a way of upsetting your plans, or your mistress.'
She swallowed and then lied bitterly, 'Even if it has to
be Ewan Cameron.'

'So nothing happened between you two, then?' enquired Neil.

'Nothing,' replied Caron shortly. 'Personally I'd rather
go to bed with you than that man.'

Neil's eyes narrowed. 'That could be arranged.'

Caron breathed in with an effort. Her chest seemed
suddenly constricted by iron bands. 'Haven't you considered that I could ruin everything?' she said slowly. 'I
could just tell you that I'm not going through with this
wedding.'

Neil gripped her wrist. 'Don't be ridiculous.'

She wrenched her hand away. 'Why not? What's to
stop me?'

'You must be spectacularly naïve, Caron, if you think
I wouldn't publish those papers I have implicating your
father in fraud.'

Caron swallowed. 'I don't know why I thought you
were so pleasant when I first met you,' she said at last.

'Probably because I went out of my way to be nice to
you,' he replied. 'Although God knows it was difficult.
I spent a lot of money on you, Caron, taking you out
to dinner and the theatre.'

'Well,' she replied, 'maybe that's why. You always
think in terms of money. And in any case,' she added
practically, 'I'm not totally dim. I found out recently

that you put the cost of all those nights out down as expenses for entertaining clients.

'If you knew me one tenth as well as you think you do, you'd realise that if you'd been honest about your lack of money I'd have been much happier going for a Coke and a hamburger.'

'Don't be ridiculous,' snapped Neil. 'When did you ever want anything that didn't cost the earth?'

Caron swallowed. After I met Ewan Cameron, she thought silently. When it was far too late.

She sighed. Begging was not her forte, but the idea of marrying this man was becoming more and more repellent by the minute. 'Please don't force me to marry you,' she whispered.

'Half the women in New York are in love with Ewan Cameron,' he said brutally, 'so what chance do think you'll have of keeping him?'

'I'm not in love with Ewan!' she cried.

He grabbed her wrist again. 'Then you must be the only person who doesn't realise it,' he hissed. 'But in this case my feelings come first. We made a deal, Caron, and you're going to honour it.'

'Deal?' she said gently. 'Blackmail is a better word, don't you think?'

'If you like,' he replied sharply. 'But we made a bargain and neither of us is going to let your father down. Are we?'

'I gave you my word,' said Caron tiredly. 'We both know how much is at stake.'

He nodded slowly. 'Good,' he said. 'Good.' And then, standing so close to her that she had to close her eyes to block him out, he murmured, 'You looked very nice tonight, Caron.'

'Thank you,' she replied woodenly. His hand was on her arm now, stroking it, and she resisted the impulse to slap him in the face.

'Very nice indeed,' he added, turning her towards him.

'No, Neil,' she protested as his intentions became all too clear. 'No.'

His arms went around her and she felt physically sick. 'Why not?' he countered. 'After all, we'll be man and wife tomorrow, and you won't refuse me then, will you?'

Caron licked dry lips. 'You really must be mad if you think I'd let you make love to me,' she whispered. 'That wasn't part of the bargain at all.'

'I don't see why not,' he replied unpleasantly. 'Because when it comes to this bargain I hold all the aces.'

'What about Kate?' she demanded.

'Kate will still be here when we get back from our honeymoon,' he said. 'She's not going to run out on me, considering I'm just about to become very rich on your money.'

Something in Caron suddenly seemed to snap. 'Get away from me,' she gasped, pushing hard against him. But he was just too strong for her. Desperately she stamped on his foot with her stiletto heel, but after an initial shout of rage he only grabbed her more painfully.

'No, Neil,' she shouted. 'No!' She summoned up her energy for one last desperate kick then suddenly realised that there was nothing there.

She stood, shaking, taking in the fact that Neil was sprawled in her mother's lily pond and Ewan was standing in front of her, a rip in his shirt and blood on his cheek.

'You all right?' he said, breathing deeply but his words quiet enough.

She nodded. 'My own fault,' she mumbled.

A pulse was thudding in his cheek. 'No,' he said flatly. 'The blame for what has just happened rests entirely on someone else's shoulders.' He turned back to Neil, who was flailing desperately in the lily pond.

'Can you hear me, Smith?' he enquired.

In answer Neil swore fluently, tried to get up, and fell back again. Caron was reminded irresistibly of the horse trough.

Ewan squatted down by the pond and stared at Neil. 'When you get out of there I would go straight home if I were you. You needn't go in the house.'

He paused and Neil swore again. Ewan got up and dusted off his jacket. 'But while you're in there,' he added, 'you might as well wash your mouth out.'

And, taking Caron's arm, he headed back to the house.

CHAPTER NINE

'CARON!' exclaimed her mother as they re-entered the room. 'What on earth has happened? You look like you've been dragged through a hedge backwards.'

'She fell in a rose bush,' supplied Ewan, sucking his hand. 'Unfortunately Neil had already gone home, and I just happened to be passing, so to speak.'

'Gone home?' Kate looked at all of them, a queer desperate expression on her face. 'But he promised me a lift. I—'

Ewan smiled at her and Caron had the sudden desire to smash something large and heavy on his head. 'It would be my pleasure to give you a ride home, ma'am,' he drawled, and without one backward glance at Caron he helped Kate into her wrap, held the door open for her and followed her out.

'Caron?' questioned her mother in the following silence. 'You really look quite upset, dear. What happened out there? You and Neil haven't rowed, have you?'

It was ironic, Caron thought, how pleased her mother looked at the prospect of a rift between her and Neil. 'No, not at all,' she replied. 'I just...I just have a headache, that's all.'

Her father reached out for her hand. 'Are you sure you want to go through with this wedding?'

Caron swallowed. She simply couldn't believe that her father was guilty of fraud. But those papers proved that he had to be, and she couldn't bear the thought of him being exposed to all the contempt that would surely follow if the secret got out. 'Absolutely,' she said as firmly as she could.

Her mother smiled at her and changed the subject. 'Wasn't it nice of Ewan to take Kate home? Don't you think they're attracted to each other? They certainly seemed to get on very well.' She shook her head. 'It must be this wedding, but I seem to be jumping to as many conclusions these days as you do, Caron.'

Caron's jaw sagged. 'Who told you I jump to conclusions?' she demanded.

Her mother gazed at her in astonishment. 'Why, no one, of course. I do happen to be your mother. And it is your main fault.'

Even now, after Ewan had left the room, he seemed to be standing right next to her, the words 'I told you so' on his lips.

Caron shook her head as if to rid her mind of such an unwelcome picture, only to conjure up instantly instead the idea of Ewan and Kate together.

Her father put his hands on her shoulders and broke the spell. 'You look tired, darling. Don't worry about Neil. Everybody has tiffs before they marry.' He smiled at his wife. 'We certainly did. Everything will sort itself out, believe me. Now go to bed and take some aspirin, and in the morning everything will be fine.'

Wearily Caron sat in front of her mirror and wiped off her make-up. Tomorrow she would be Mrs Neil Smith. The prospect ought to have appalled her, but all she could think about was Ewan. She had come upstairs with the full intention of going straight to bed. But now, alone at last, sleep was the last thing on her mind.

She had kept telling him that she wanted him to stay in the Rockies, although if she was honest with herself

she didn't know how she would have got through the
last week without his company. Now, with each passing
day it was even more impossible for him to stay so close
to her, but it would be a very bleak world without him.

What on earth was he up to, swanning off with Kate
like that? She screwed a piece of tissue paper up and
threw it at her reflection.

She couldn't have meant that much to him after all,
even if he had come all the way from Canada with her,
she thought with a rush of self-pity. He had business
interests in London and she was just good entertainment
value until something else came along. Like that civil-
servant woman he had mentioned, she thought viciously,
and how he'd had the absolute gall to take Kate home
she would never know. Hours ago, too. He was probably
still with her.

Awful pictures of what they could be doing together
ran again through her mind. She shook her head and
then rubbed her hands distractedly through her hair. He
wouldn't be making love to Kate. He just wouldn't.
Would he?

As if on cue, a handful of gravel spattered against her
bedroom window.

Caron turned around in sudden fear. Please, God, let
it not be Neil, she prayed silently. Another shower of
gravel hit the window and she stared at it, dumbfounded,
before opening the curtains and looking down.

It was Ewan.

He had put a ladder against the wall and was climbing
it with the determination of a hungry panther.

She opened the window. 'What on earth do you think
you are doing?' she whispered fiercely.

His head came level with hers. 'You could say I'm
paying a social call,' he said.

'But it's one a.m.,' she said hoarsely.

'My kind of time,' he grinned. He put one leg over her window-sill and swung himself into her room. 'Wouldn't want to disturb Mrs Peabody, would we?' he said, smiling infuriatingly at her.

'I wasn't aware that I was,' she replied icily. 'You're the one who's doing all the disturbing.'

He pulled her to him and kissed her full on the lips. 'Well, that's nice to know,' he murmured.

She struggled out of his arms, her heart thumping, and gazed at him furiously. 'Where the hell have you been?' she demanded.

He raised his eyebrows and smiled slowly at her. 'You practising for when you get married?'

Caron flushed. 'You've been out with Kate,' she snapped. 'And you've been drinking.'

Ewan lay back on her bed and eased off his tie. 'Correct on both counts,' he drawled, knotting the black silk in a bow around the neck of her old teddy bear. 'I've been having a very interesting evening. But my, it sure takes a lot to get that girl drunk.'

Her eyes narrowed. 'If you had to get her drunk to get her into bed, then she's choosier than I thought,' she snarled.

'And I thought you were so ladylike when I met you,' Ewan replied mockingly, closing his eyes and settling more comfortably on her bed, the bear staring with glassy-eyed contentment from his arms.

Caron stepped towards him. 'How dare you come back here after seducing my fiancé's mistress?'

Ewan chuckled. 'If you could only hear yourself,' he murmured. 'What are you going to do? Tell Neil?'

Caron bit her lip. 'If I have to,' she said coldly.

Ewan sighed. 'For such a nicely brought up girl you really have an awfully sordid imagination. Not to mention a deep insecurity complex.'

'You're the one who's got a complex,' she retorted. 'About women. You see one and you just have to have her. I'm surprised you haven't tried anything on with Mrs Peabody.'

He clasped his hands behind his head and grinned at her. 'Is that why you beat her to the door tonight? Afraid I'd be enslaved by her charms?'

'Stop twisting my words and get out of my room immediately,' she hissed. 'I never want to see you again. Ever.'

There was silence from the bed. 'Ewan?' she said, stepping closer. But there was no reply. It seemed that he had fallen asleep. She marched up to him furiously. How dared he do this to her? How dared he? But when she leant over him to shake him awake his arms slid around her and he pulled her onto the bed beside him.

'That's better,' he sighed. 'Your teddy's all very well, but he doesn't have anything like your legs. We can get some sleep now.'

She pushed at him ineffectually. 'Get some sleep in your own house, you rotten creep.'

'Such language,' he said softly, kissing her throat. Whatever he had been drinking it was all too obvious that he was a very long way from being drunk.

'How do you expect me to react?' she said, almost in tears. 'I feel like you've betrayed me. How could you stoop so low?'

'Despicable is my middle name, remember?' drawled Ewan. 'Besides, sweetheart, you're the one who's getting married to someone else.'

Caron thought of her conversation with Neil and swallowed hard. 'I have to marry him,' she said stiffly. 'It's a matter of family honour.'

'Your family honour can rot in hell before I see you marry him,' he retorted, his arms tightening around her, all pretence at sleepiness evaporating.

'Why should you care?' she demanded, struggling to get away from him.

He let her go and she scrambled to the other side of the bed, her cheeks flushed, the blood thundering in her ears. Ewan propped himself up on one elbow and stared at her. 'Do you keep trying to jump over there because that's where you keep your conclusions?' he drawled.

She breathed deeply, suddenly aware that with the bedside light shining on her her sheer nightdress was almost completely see-through. 'Go away,' she said desperately, trying to cover herself with her hands.

'Caron,' he said gently, 'you need my help.'

'I need your help like I need a hole in the head,' she retorted.

His eyes were like deep lakes under a summer sky. 'Trust me,' he persisted softly.

'I'd rather trust Neil,' she snapped. 'At least he's honest about what he wants.'

There were storm clouds over those lakes now, and Caron shivered.

'Honest, huh?' Ewan grated, reaching out for her, his hand encircling her wrist as surely as a handcuff and drawing her towards him.

'Ewan, please,' she muttered, but it was like pleading with a grizzly bear.

'What did he tell you he wanted, when he was trying to blackmail you, Caron?'

'Forget it,' she said desperately. 'Please. We're just getting married, that's all.'

'"Just getting married",' he repeated softly, dangerously. 'Is that because he finds you so attractive?'

She ran her tongue over dry lips. 'Maybe,' she muttered.

He looked at her for a long moment and then released her wrist. 'Have you ever slept with a man, Caron?'

Her heart seemed to do a double somersault and she swallowed hard. Trust him to ask such a direct question. 'Slept with him or made love with him?' she asked as boldly as she could.

He leaned towards her, his eyes never leaving hers. 'You tell me.'

She could feel the colour rising up her neck and spreading like red dye across her face. 'I don't have to tell you anything,' she muttered.

'No,' he sighed. 'I guess you don't. I can read the answer in your eyes.'

There was a look of gentleness on his face that brought a lump to her throat. 'I just don't understand, that's all,' he said. 'You're—what? Twenty-four? And—'

'Twenty-five,' she corrected him.

'Twenty-five, then,' he smiled. 'And you still haven't had a love affair. Why not?'

Caron was silent. She traced the pattern on her quilt with a forefinger and then looked him straight in the eye. 'I suppose I just never found anyone I wanted an affair with before.'

'That day in the forest—' he began.

'It was an error in judgement,' she said quickly—too quickly.

He reached out and touched her face. 'Funny,' he smiled. 'I thought that was almost the best decision you'd ever made. Pity we didn't carry it to its natural conclusion.'

She gripped his fingers, her eyes bright with unshed tears. 'I don't want to talk about it,' she whispered. 'I just can't. Not now. Not tonight.'

He sighed and looked at her with an expression she couldn't quite fathom.

'Anyway, what difference does my still being a virgin make?' she muttered fiercely.

'It makes a difference to you,' he said. 'Especially when Neil curls up in bed with you tomorrow night.'

Caron glared at him. 'It's not going to be like that,' she snarled. 'Neil and I have made a deal. Purely business. We are not going to sleep together.'

'Uh-huh,' Ewan nodded, the expression on his face revealing that he was anything but convinced.

'Don't you "uh-huh" me,' snapped Caron. 'You know nothing about it.'

'I know what I saw in the garden tonight,' said Ewan. 'Wise up, Caron. Neil's a blackmailer; why on earth do you think that any deal you struck with him is going to hold?'

The blush had reached her forehead now; she could almost feel it seeping into her scalp. 'Because I have to,' she whispered.

'You going to tell Neil?' he said softly.

She shook her head. 'I can't see that he'd be very interested,' she replied stiffly.

'Oh, I think he's very interested in you,' Ewan contradicted her. 'Or is it, by some faint chance, your money that he's more attracted to?'

Caron swallowed. 'Don't be ridiculous. Now you're the one jumping to conclusions.'

He stretched his legs more comfortably on the bed and looked at her assessingly.

'What is it? What's the matter?' she demanded.

He shrugged. 'Nothing, except that you don't seem to be able to keep your story straight at all. You'd make a lousy criminal.'

'Thank you,' she snapped.

'You're welcome,' he said, a lazy smile lifting the corners of his eyes. 'But one moment you're telling me you really do love Neil, the next that you're not going to sleep with him.'

Caron opened her mouth to stop him in his tracks but Ewan swept on inexorably. 'If you love him, why the need for him to blackmail you into marriage? Unless, of course, it's something to do with this sense of family honour you keep letting slip about.'

'No need at all,' whispered Caron, her heart pounding. 'I told you, I was just exaggerating about the blackmail. It was all a big misunderstanding. We...we talked it all through in the garden and everything's fine.'

'How fine?' said Ewan. 'So fine that you'll be letting him make love to you like this tomorrow night?' And, pulling her towards him, his hands slid under the sheer silk of her nightdress.

'Don't do this, Ewan; please let me go,' she gasped.

'Is that what you're going to say to him?' he demanded remorselessly.

'I told you, I'm not going to make love with him,' she said wildly.

His eyes were like pools of ink now. 'Is that what you were talking about in the garden this evening?' he demanded harshly.

'I—no—yes!' she replied desperately.

His hands withdrew from her heated skin, leaving a trail of ice in their wake. Ice that one day, she knew, would encase her heart.

He took off his jacket, extracted a long brown envelope from the inside pocket and then turned to face Caron. 'Why don't you just tell me the truth about the hold he's got over you, hmm?'

'I can't—' she began, but he silenced her with one contemptuous wave of his hand.

'Don't give me that,' he snarled. 'Do you think I'm as stupid as Neil?'

Caron pulled a sheet around her, more for the impression of protective covering than warmth. Although, the way Ewan was looking at her, even a bullet-proof vest wouldn't have given her much protection.

'Well?' he demanded. 'I'm waiting.'

'I can't tell you anything,' she muttered.

He threw the envelope between them on the bed. 'Because of some outdated idea about saving your father's honour, and stopping Neil from telling everyone what an expert fraudster he is?'

Caron gasped. 'How—how do you know about that?' she breathed.

He stared at her with those unrelenting blue eyes, then shrugged. 'I'm not psychic, Caron, if that's what you mean. But you're not exactly the best liar I've ever come across, or, for that matter, the best lawyer.'

'You don't know anything about my skills as a lawyer,' she flashed.

A faint hint of humour came into his eyes. 'I'm the poor cowboy who was going to be so grateful for the big inheritance, remember? Only trouble was, you didn't even know what the inheritance was. And when—'

'All right, all right!' snapped Caron. 'So I didn't impress you very much, and I can't blame you, I suppose. I must have looked very stupid. But I was under a great deal of stress.'

Ewan nodded. 'So I discovered that morning after that nightmare you had. When I dug out those papers from your suitcase about Cousin William's bequest, I also found some particularly interesting ones about your father's attempts to defraud a woman client of his.'

Caron gazed at him, thunderstruck. 'How come you still have those documents?'

'I copied them,' he said simply. 'I wanted to have a really good look at them without you dancing up and down and tearing your hair out about how it was none of my business.'

'Well, it isn't,' flashed Caron, making an ineffectual grab for them.

'That's where you are wrong,' he replied. 'It was your father who prepared my cousin's will. How do I know he didn't defraud him too?'

His accusation was like icy water in her face. 'Is that all you care about?' she forced out. 'Money?'

'Among other things,' he nodded. 'Like honesty and fair dealing.'

'Well, go and look for it elsewhere,' she cried. 'Like under the nearest stone with all your closest relations.'

'Keep your voice down,' he ordered in a low voice. 'We don't want the whole house crowding in here.'

'You might not,' said Caron defiantly, 'but why should I care? I've done nothing to be ashamed of.'

He moved towards her, over the bed. 'No?' he said.

'No,' she repeated with a bravado she did not feel.

He smiled challengingly at her. 'What would happen if I reached across right now and pulled you into bed with me? Of course,' he added, 'I'd take my clothes off first. How would you explain your way out of that?'

She swallowed rapidly. 'You wouldn't dare.'

'I've already taken my jacket and tie off,' he said musingly. 'What would you like next? Shirt or trousers?'

'Ewan, please!' she pleaded.

He looked at her eyes, as blue as his, and stopped. 'I'm sorry,' he said gently. 'But there are more people involved in this mess than just you.'

She clasped her hands together and then looked up into his face. 'Sir William was Father's greatest friend,' she said at last. 'I know you called him a drunk, and maybe he was. But I'd known him my whole life, and I thought he was wonderful.'

Ewan shrugged. 'My mother had a way of exaggerating, I guess. I'm sorry if I upset you with those comments.'

She looked at him pleadingly. 'I'm sure the will is perfectly all right. I can't believe my father has stolen anything—from that woman client, or Sir William, or anyone else,' she said.

He reached for her hand. 'Caron—'

But she continued in a rush, 'I just can't prove it, that's all. Father is the senior partner in our law firm, you know. It would kill him if those documents were published. I can't even talk to him about them. He's already had one heart attack. A shock like that could kill him.'

Ewan stared at her. 'And you're willing to sacrifice your life to save his?'

She nodded numbly. 'There's no other way out,' she said softly.

'You're throwing your whole life away, Caron,' he said harshly. 'Do you have any idea what it's going to be like, living with that bastard Neil?'

'He's only after my money,' muttered Caron unconvincingly. 'I take over my trust fund in two years' time and that's what he's really after. It will give him the kind of lifestyle he's always wanted, and marrying me will give him a head start when it comes to promotion.'

She flashed him a look tinged with some of her old spirit. 'Ironic, isn't it,' she remarked, 'that he is really after my money, when you used to think I was probably after his?'

She smiled faintly at Ewan's grim face, before adding, 'When I've signed over the cash to him he will agree to divorce me.'

'That's big of him,' said Ewan coldly. 'I must say, though, for a woman pushed to the brink you certainly seem to have thought it all through very carefully.'

Caron lifted her hands helplessly. 'Neil told me,' she said. 'He laid it all out for me to see. He always did have a very clear mind.'

Ewan swung himself off the bed. 'I'm damned if I'm going to stand here all night talking about Neil,' he said. 'Where's your suitcase?'

'Suitcase?' repeated Caron uncertainly.

He looked at her and shrugged. 'Maybe you're right. You can't climb down a ladder with a suitcase. Get a plastic carrier bag and put what you need in that.'

Caron gazed at him. 'Just what are you talking about?'

He shrugged his jacket on. 'I'm talking about you, Caron. And the fact that you are not going to spend another night where Neil can get at you.'

'I'm marrying him tomorrow,' she flashed.

'I don't think so,' he snapped. He looked up—and stilled as he saw her wedding dress hanging ready on her wardrobe door. 'This what you were planning on wearing?'

She nodded, unable to speak as he unzipped its polythene bag and took a long look at the frothy lace. He turned to her, his face a mask. 'You going to be wearing the plastic covering as well?'

She swallowed. 'Don't be silly,' she choked. 'It's to protect the material.'

He stepped towards her. 'It's not the dress that needs protection, Caron, it's you.'

'I'm perfectly capable of taking care of myself,' she retorted.

'So I saw this evening,' he said drily. 'Now get dressed and get packed, or so help me you are going down that ladder in your nightdress.'

'I'm not going anywhere with you,' she said rebelliously.

He took a step towards her and with a strangled cry she swept up a bundle of clothes and hurried into her bathroom.

'This is just ridiculous,' she said for the tenth time fifteen minutes later, sitting on the window-sill and trying hard not to look down at the ground outside.

'So is marrying a blackmailer,' replied Ewan.

'And I don't like heights,' she added.

'Neither do I,' he softly. 'Remember?'

She thought of the clifftop and swallowed. 'You don't have to do this for me,' she said softly. 'You could just go away and forget all about me.'

He gazed at her expressionlessly. 'It's just my misfortune that I happen to have an extremely good memory.'

Her lips parted. 'Running away won't solve anything,' she said.

'Is that something new that you've just learned?' he enquired. 'Because you certainly weren't abiding by that notion when you ran six thousand miles to get away from Neil.'

Caron flushed but said nothing. 'In any case,' Ewan continued, 'we're not running away. You could say I'm placing you in protective custody until I can get this mess sorted out.'

'"Protective custody"?' she repeated.

He nodded. 'Yes. Mine.'

For one infinitesimal part of a second her heart leapt and then she shrugged helplessly. 'Tell me the truth, Ewan. Whatever I may feel about those documents, do you think they are genuine?'

He said nothing. She lifted her hand to his cheek, looking him straight in the eye. 'Do you?'

He looked at her for a long moment and said tonelessly, 'It would seem, at the moment, that there is no other explanation.'

'If someone showed you those documents and they concerned someone who worked for you,' she continued remorselessly, 'what would you do?'

Ewan looked bleak. 'I'd fire them,' he replied.

'And if you think that way,' she said, 'then why shouldn't everyone else? What can you do in so short a time?'

'I'm working on it,' he said firmly. 'Now get down that ladder.'

She looked into his eyes once more and then, without another word, put her foot on the top rung of the ladder and began climbing down.

The warm night was heavy with the smell of cow parsley and new grass as they made their way along the old footpath to the manor house. There was a full moon tipping the countryside with silver and Caron felt her spirits rise.

Then a sudden thought struck her and she smiled to herself.

'What?' Ewan demanded. 'What's so funny?'

'It's not funny, really,' she said softly. 'It's just that when I met Neil I thought he was a really nice person. So attentive and kind. And when I met you...' She smiled again.

'Yes?' prompted Ewan grimly.

'Well,' she giggled, 'I thought you were the most awful man I'd ever met. So arrogant, and forcing me to do your housework like that. The day you threw that jug of water over me I wanted to leap out of bed and strangle you.'

'Shame you didn't strangle Neil,' he rasped.

'I didn't realise what he was up to until it was too late,' she admitted. 'I found him and Kate together one day and told him that was it. But he just calmly announced that we were going to get married ... and why. He even gave me that revolting picture of himself. He put it in my handbag and told me I was to look at it every day. I'd have torn it up, but I thought it had dropped out.'

'I wondered about that,' he said idly. 'I couldn't see why you were carrying the picture of a guy who was blackmailing you. It seemed perverse, to say the least.'

They were in front of the manor now, and Ewan reached into his pocket for his keys.

'Oh, I'm a very perverse woman,' replied Caron lightly. 'Look at me, traipsing round the countryside with another man the night before my wedding.'

He pushed open the door and then turned to her, his face thrown into sharp relief by the moon's radiance. 'As far as I'm concerned this is your wedding night,' he said softly.

His fingers brushed her cheek and she trembled as he reached for her hand, led her into the house, and, closing the door behind them, led her up the stairs.

He paused by the bedroom door and pulled her close. 'I don't know how you've done it, Caron, but I just can't stop thinking about you,' he said grimly. 'The way you smile, the way you look when you're angry; I can't stop looking at you and I can't get you out of my mind.'

She looked up at him, her heart thudding against her ribs. 'You could try closing your eyes,' she said shakily.

A slow smile curved his lips. 'That makes it even worse, because then I see you all the time.'

He bent to kiss her, and then drew back, staring intently into her eyes. 'It's no good, Caron,' he grated. 'I want you like I've wanted no other woman.'

'You're just so sure, aren't you?' she forced out. 'But there are some pretty heavy odds stacked against you, you know.'

'Maybe,' he shrugged. 'But I have the edge.'

She stared at him in the moonlight. 'What?'

'I have you,' he growled. 'And possession is nine tenths of the law.' Hooking her knees under his arm, he carried her to his bed, which was flooded in silver from the light streaming through the window.

'I'm not a possession,' she said weakly as he lay down beside her, his hand tangling in her hair.

'No,' he agreed softly, 'but you're mine, just the same.'

Instinctively her hands reached up to ease off his jacket, and then slid between the buttons on his shirt. The breath jerked in her throat as his hand halted her fingers and he undid the buttons himself.

His body was so beautiful, she thought as he leant over her, his fingers brushing tantalisingly against her quivering skin as he began to unfasten her shirt, then stripped away her cotton skirt.

'This must be wrong,' she murmured.

His mouth kissed her throat, her jaw, and hovered over her lips. 'Why?' he said softly.

'Because it feels so right,' she admitted shakily.

'Good,' he whispered.

Her hands tangled around his neck and then stroked down the warm smoothness of his back. Her eyes closed with pleasure and then flicked open; she gazed at him directly. 'Maybe it's wrong,' she breathed. 'Maybe I should be stronger or something, but it doesn't seem to matter what you do, Ewan, I know I'll never feel this way about anyone else.'

She swallowed then added softly, 'I don't even care about Kate, or your strange new woman in the civil service.'

She looked at him, an unspoken plea in her eyes, and his lips curved. 'There's nothing there for you to care about,' he said. 'There is only you, as far as I'm concerned.' He smiled right into her eyes. 'I'll tell you all about it later,' he promised. 'But not now.'

'No,' she agreed, her breath catching in her throat. 'Not now.'

He lifted her fingers to his lips before his hands dropped to cup the full softness of her breasts. 'You are the only one,' he repeated, his fingers trailing down over her vulnerable skin.

She gasped at the touch of his warm mouth moving over her heated flesh, wanting nothing more than to please him, but not sure how. Her hands moved instinctively over his chest; she was barely aware of the effect she was having on him. 'Oh, Ewan,' she breathed. 'I've never—'

'I know,' he said softly. 'I know. And now you will always be mine. Only mine.' Her senses reeled under the simple sureness of his touch, her eyes cloudy with desire; she was unable to speak, unable to think. 'I've wanted you for so long,' he breathed raggedly, his voice thick with passion, pushing her down into the softness of the bed.

She pulled him to her, wanting him, needing him, her first tentative moves growing more sure as he carried along on the tide of their mutual discovery. Her every nerve-ending responded to his slightest touch, until reason receded and was replaced by only feelings, their desires merging until, a small cry escaping from her throat, he was with her completely as she had always yearned for him to be.

CHAPTER TEN

IT WAS late the next morning when Caron awoke. She sighed with sleepy pleasure and rolled over with a feeling of luxurious happiness to put her arms round Ewan.

But there was no one there. And the indent in the sheets, showing where he had lain, was cold.

Pushing her fingers confusedly through her hair, she sat up. Then, dragging a sheet off the bed and wrapping it round herself, she went in search of him.

Perhaps he was making tea, or, more likely, coffee. She smiled to herself at the memory of the night they had met. It was hardly likely that Ewan would be mixing up bourbon at this time of the day.

But as she shouted his name through the old house she soon had to come to the conclusion that he had gone. But where? Surely he would have told her what he wanted her to do if he really was working on something to prove her father innocent?

She peered through the leaded windows to see if he was outside, but all she could see was the pink and white striped marquee erected for the wedding reception in her parents' garden.

Her wedding. The thought struck a chill through her body and she climbed the stairs to dress. It was eleven-thirty—if Ewan didn't work the miracle he had promised she would be walking up the aisle in four hours' time.

Wearily she gathered up her clothes from the floor where Ewan had thrown them the night before, hoping all the time that she would hear the sound of a car, or his voice, but all she could hear was pure sweet birdsong and the sound of church bells. Bells tolling now as they would later for her and Neil, she thought, her heart thudding.

She took as long as she could over dressing in order to delay the moment when she had to make a decision. But it was no use. The minutes ticked away and nothing was happening to alter her predicament.

What was she going to do? Ewan had seemed so positive last night that he could help her, but now he had simply disappeared.

She swallowed and thought numbly of the night before. What had Ewan said to her? That he wanted her, certainly. But he had never once said that he really felt anything for her. That he loved her. Had it all been a trick? A mean ploy to get her into bed?

She shook her head confusedly. That was something she could believe of Neil, but Ewan... He was completely different. He couldn't have deserted her, surely?

Tentatively she walked outside and searched the garages. There was no sign of the car he had rented at the airport. Nothing. He had definitely gone. Numbly she considered her options, and realised with a sickening awareness that she hadn't any.

Whatever Ewan had done, her situation was still the same. If she didn't show up at the church as planned Neil would show those documents to the police. She closed her eyes as she thought of her father.

What had Neil said? That every woman in New York was after Ewan. She had seen with her own eyes how he had so easily attracted Kate. For a predator surely it would be the ultimate coup, Caron thought bitterly, to seduce a man's mistress and his bride.

Her head sagging in her hands, she thought of Ewan and the way he had made her come alive in the past week...the feelings he had awoken in her the night before. How could he have run out on her now?

She looked at her watch once more. Twelve-thirty. She was going to have to do something, and soon. Predator. The word thudded through her brain once more. Ewan had denied it that day in the forest, but maybe she had been right all along. Whatever he'd said about her jumping to conclusions, events now merely showed that she had simply jumped to the wrong ones.

How could she have shown him that she was so vulnerable? Her heart ached as she thought of his words of tenderness, the way he had touched her. But the bitterness that had so long been battened down in her soul came flooding out as she realised that without him she was completely sunk.

Maybe he had said all those things to her just to get her into bed. And now, after that, it wouldn't matter what happened to her.

Racked by doubts and uncertainty, she lifted her head and gave one single piercing scream of anguish which echoed through the old house. Then, stiffly, she stood up. Ewan was not going to come back, that much was obvious. Wherever he had gone, it was time to keep her part of the bargain she had made so unwillingly with Neil.

The bang of the front door as she closed it behind her reverberated through the whole house and a folded piece of paper that had fallen behind her pillow fluttered to the floor. Scrawled across the top of it was her name, in Ewan's handwriting.

* * *

'Darling!' exclaimed Mrs Lane as Caron walked into the sitting room. 'Where have you been?'

'It's a very long story, Mother,' she muttered, collapsing wearily into an easy chair.

Mrs Lane gazed at her in astonishment. 'I just went up to wake you, dear, and the door was locked.'

'Was it?' asked Caron innocently, her heart thumping. 'Must have been jammed somehow. I got up early and went for a walk. Couldn't sleep.'

'You ought to have something to eat and then start getting ready,' advised her mother gently.

Caron swallowed and then shook her head. 'Think I'll skip eating,' she said numbly. 'Even the idea of food...'

Mrs Lane smiled understandingly. 'It's just nerves. You'll feel better after the ceremony.'

'Maybe,' replied Caron listlessly.

'Neil's been on the phone.' Her mother looked at her, obviously waiting for an enthusiastic response.

'Oh?' responded Caron.

Her mother nodded. 'Seemed very cheerful, I must say. He's giving Kate a lift to the wedding. Which is most considerate of him, if you think of the hundred and one things he must be thinking of. Maybe I misjudged him.'

Caron's jaw dropped. 'Kate?' she whispered.

Her mother looked at her more closely. 'Is there something wrong, dear? I believe they live quite close to each other.'

'Yes,' nodded Caron numbly. She had not realised that Kate was coming to the wedding. Had not really thought about it. But now, in a day of hurting, this trivial gesture seemed set to put the seal on her feelings.

'When I said I thought you were asleep,' her mother continued, 'he told me I could guarantee getting you up and out on time simply by reminding you of some little secret you share.'

Caron shivered and then looked hopefully at her mother. 'Ewan didn't ring, did he?'

Mrs Lane looked blankly at her. 'Ewan? I don't think so. He told us before that he wouldn't make it to the wedding. I suppose he must be flying back to Canada today. Shame, really, I think, that you didn't meet him before all this. Your characters are so perfectly matched. Still...'

Mrs Lane lifted her hands helplessly as she saw her daughter's eyes fill with sudden tears. 'Oh, darling, I'm sorry if I was tactless. I thought you disliked Ewan, you were so rude to him.'

'I did dislike him,' said Caron stiffly. 'And you haven't been tactless. It's just that we're both bundles of nerves. Getting married is supposed to affect you like that, so I hear.'

Her mother opened her mouth but no words came out. Caron, her last vestige of hope withering, turned to the door. 'I'll go and get ready,' she said quietly.

The dress was cold on her skin as her mother slipped it over her head. 'There,' said Mrs Lane, putting the finishing touch to her veil. 'You look beautiful.' Her bottom lip trembled and she patted Caron quickly on the cheek before turning and hurrying out of the room.

Caron glanced at her two cousins, charming in their bridesmaid's outfits. 'Ready?' she asked.

'Oh, we're all right,' said the elder, Sue, with all the withering forthrightness of a fifteen-year-old. 'But what about you?'

'What do you mean?' snapped Caron, wondering with a jolt if her cousin could somehow tell what she was thinking.

The girls exchanged glances. 'Well, you don't seem exactly happy,' said the younger girl, Wendy.

'I'm just nervous, that's all,' Caron retorted, sweeping out of the room. 'It's perfectly normal to be nervous before you get married, apparently. Now come on and let's get this blasted thing over with.'

The distance from the house to the church was so short that Caron usually walked. She looked apprehensively at the big car waiting in the drive. 'Silly to have gone to all the trouble of ordering one, really, Dad,' she said. 'We'll get there before we've started out.'

Mr Lane patted her arm. 'No, we won't. And stop worrying. It's your wedding day, the sun is shining and everything will be fine. The driver's got strict instructions to take a big detour. Wouldn't do to have you arriving on time, would it?'

She shook her head and climbed in. It didn't matter how much of a detour they made, she would still end up marrying a man she hated. While the man she loved... She blinked away the tears welling up in her eyes. Ewan had gone. She had to face up to that. He had taken what he wanted and gone.

'We're here,' her father said gently, breaking in on her thoughts. He looked at her face for a long moment. 'Is there anything you want to tell me, darling?'

Caron swallowed. 'Like what?'

He shrugged. 'You don't have to go through with this, you know. You can always back out now.'

'Don't be silly,' she said in a rush of affection for the man sitting next to her. A man for whom she would hazard everything. 'I couldn't possibly back out now. Not after all the trouble you and Mummy have been through.'

Her father looked her in the eye. 'I wouldn't blame you if you did,' he said. 'Neither of us would, you know. We just want you to be happy.'

Caron looked at his face and thought how well he had recovered since that dreadful day of his collapse. She felt her throat constricting at the idea of what might happen if he ever saw those incriminating papers. 'I'm all right,' she forced out. 'Really.'

Her father nodded as though not entirely convinced. 'Maybe it's not the time to mention Ewan,' he said. 'But I thought—that is, your mother and I hoped—'

'You're right,' cut in Caron desperately. 'It's not the time to discuss him. I . . . We . . .' She stopped and shook her head helplessly as the car drew to a halt. 'Come on, Dad,' she said at last. 'Time to go and all that.'

Her father sighed deeply and then helped her out of the car. A little knot of onlookers sighed in appreciation as she emerged, Sue and Wendy straightening her dress and veil. Her head high, she could see no sign of Ewan. Well, that was it. He had definitely gone.

Her father held out his arm, and they could hear the organist begin to play the 'Bridal March'. 'They're playing your tune, Caron,' he told her softly.

Smiling weakly, her hand on her father's arm, she began the seemingly endless walk to the altar. Why, even now, did she keep hoping to get a glimpse of Ewan? But even as she scanned the pews, packed with friends and relations, she knew he was not there. Not even one of the old stone pillars could have hidden his tall, distinctive form.

The one person she did recognise in the sea of faces was Kate, a strange mixture of triumph and jealousy on her smart pale face.

Neil was standing up now, waiting for her to arrive at his side, and she stilled the urge to turn tail and flee. She looked at her father and then straight ahead. There was simply no alternative.

The service began but the vicar's words seemed meaningless, as if he were speaking some foreign language. They merely flowed over her.

Neil's hand was cold on hers and she tugged her fingers away. She might have struck a bargain with him, but he was mistaken if he thought there was going to be any contact between them. That had been reserved solely for a man she thought she loved and who had now deserted her.

The congregation stirred a little at this sign of strange rebelliousness and then stilled again as everyone knelt to pray. Caron knew that Neil was shooting her furious looks, but she ignored him, intent instead on reading the words on the memorial stone in front of her. Anything to get her through this ordeal. They stood up again to sing a hymn, and she found that she could open her mouth but no words seemed to want to come out.

Her veil seemed to weigh a ton and she longed to rip it from her head. What was the point of it all? Then the music stopped and the vicar began addressing them on the purpose of marriage.

She glanced at Neil. Well, she wasn't entering upon this lightly or thoughtlessly, that much was true, she thought bitterly as the sermon struck home.

There was a small silence and then Caron's heart thumped as the time-honoured words echoed around the old church. 'If any man can show any just cause, why they may not lawfully be joined together, let him now speak, or else hereafter for ever hold his peace.'

The vicar, hardly drawing breath, opened his mouth to continue the service when a voice Caron knew only too well said, 'There are several reasons why this couple can't marry.'

As one the congregation turned and Caron, turning with them, saw Ewan framed in the doorway; he began to walk up the aisle with his long, easy stride.

He stopped by her side and, taking her hand, stared down into her eyes, but there was no particular softness in his expression. 'Why the hell didn't you stay at the manor like I told you?' he demanded.

She glared at him. 'Because you ran out on me,' she snapped. 'And I had a rather pressing appointment at the church.'

Ewan's lips twitched. 'Well, I've just cancelled it.'

The vicar looked at him in blank amazement and then took off his spectacles. 'Are you telling me there is some just impediment to this marriage?'

'You're damn right I am,' drawled Ewan.

Neil, ashen-faced, opened his mouth, but the vicar raised his hand slightly. 'What is this reason?'

Ewan nodded at Neil. 'Simply that this man is already married.'

'It's a lie,' Neil hissed.

Ewan gazed at him. 'I don't think so,' he said. 'I have your marriage certificate in my pocket. There is no record of any divorce and, if that doesn't do, I have good reason to believe your wife is here.'

Neil was silent.

'True?' prompted Ewan.

'Yes, it's true,' came a low voice from the pews behind them. Kate stood up, and edged her way past shocked faces to the aisle. The sound of her heels clicking on the stone floor echoed around the walls as everyone seemed to hold their breath.

Caron looked anxiously at her father, but he seemed perfectly calm, shooting her a reassuring glance.

'It's true,' repeated Kate, standing by Neil. 'This man is my husband. We've been married for nine years.'

Neil's face was the colour of putty. He took a step back as if he was considering making a run for it but Caron's father stood up and grasped him by the arm. 'They say shocks are bad for heart-attack victims,' he mused. 'But, you know, this is one I think I could cope with rather well.'

He nodded at the vicar. 'Let's go and have a little talk in the vestry, shall we?' And, smiling at Ewan, he shepherded Neil and Kate to the door at the side of the choir stalls.

Ewan watched them go, and then, oblivious of the two hundred pairs of eyes boring into the back of his head, turned back to Caron and said softly, 'As far as that other little matter is concerned, nobody in your family is guilty of fraud.'

She stared up at him, conscious that he had thrown her cage door wide open, then flung her arms about him. 'Oh, Ewan, I do love you.'

He grinned widely and lifted her veil. 'In that case, I guess I'm just going to have to kiss the bride.'

'You did *what*?' Caron exclaimed.

Ewan shrugged. 'OK, so I bent some of the rules,' he agreed.

' "Bent them"?' she repeated. 'Tied them into knots more like. Have you any idea how important the idea of confidentiality between a solicitor and his client is?'

Ewan gazed at her and she lowered her eyes. 'You mean,' he drawled, 'you'd rather I'd obeyed all the rules to the letter and then watched from the sidelines as you and Neil got married?'

She knelt on the floor by the low window of his bedroom and stared across at her parents' house. The marquee that had been erected in their garden for her wedding had been taken up three days ago. There was just a patch of flattened grass now to show where it had been.

'You know,' she said inconsequentially, 'I found my mother singing yesterday while she wrapped up all the presents to be sent back.'

Ewan's lips curved. 'Can't say as I blame her,' he remarked.

Caron turned to him, her mind once more on what he had just been telling her. 'It's just that going to the office, and stealing the address of that woman Dad was supposed to have defrauded, and then going to see her...' Caron shrugged helplessly.

'I didn't steal it,' said Ewan patiently. 'I persuaded one of the secretaries to give it to me.'

'You gave her a letter you'd forged with my father's signature asking for it, you mean,' retorted Caron. 'How did you do that?'

Ewan knelt behind her, his hands on her shoulders. 'Quite easily,' he said. 'I have business contacts here, and they know some very interesting people both in your Fraud Squad and, let's say, outside it. A little bit of forgery was the least of my problems.

'It was a team effort, really. When I showed the police the documents Neil gave you it soon emerged that they'd had dealings with him once before, a long time ago, and he was married then.'

He sighed deeply. 'I guess Neil's major mistake was in trying to get too much. He had been milking various small accounts for years, continually juggling the figures around so that no one would notice, and then he decided to go after bigger fish like that rich woman client I went to see.'

'But how did he get the blame pinned on my father?' breathed Caron, turning to face him.

Ewan shrugged. 'Only too easily. Apparently when Neil visited her house he gave her your father's name. He told her that a couple of documents needed signing, and then calmly went away and helped himself to her bank account.

'It was a pretty ambitious leap for him, but he was banking on the fact that he could cover any debts, before they were noticed, with his other "transactions" and maybe even the money from your trust fund.'

He looked gravely at her. 'Either way, at first glance your father would appear to be to blame, because that was the name Neil gave her. And that was the name he opened his new bank account under.'

'Ewan?' She put her hand on his arm, loving the feel of his muscle under the thin material. 'There's just one more thing.'

'What?' he smiled.

She paused to screw up her courage. What would happen if he told her it wasn't any of her business?

'Well?' he prompted.

She swallowed. 'It's just that you never told me who the woman in the civil service was.'

Ewan laughed. 'Oh, her.'

She glared at him. 'Yes, her. What's so funny?'

He sighed deeply. 'You really want to know?'

'Yes, I do,' she forced out. 'I'm not an incredibly jealous person by nature, Ewan, but so many things have happened to put me off balance in recent weeks that I've just got to know about everything that's happened.'

'Everything?' he teased.

'Everything,' she said firmly.

He brushed her cheek with gentle fingers. 'Her name, for the record, was Gladys.'

'I'm not keeping records,' snapped Caron. 'I just—' She stopped, then faltered, 'Gladys?'

Ewan nodded. 'She has a mind like a steel trap and haunts the corridors of St Catherine's House.'

Caron stared at him, light beginning to dawn. 'Where they keep the birth, marriage and death certificates?'

He nodded. 'Police records showed that a Neil and Kate Smith had been married and had operated together as blackmailers. But there was nothing about a split.

'So when I took Kate home the night before the wedding I got her as drunk as a skunk and began pumping. She didn't actually admit they were married, but it was obvious that she and Neil had been close for years. They had taken separate flats for their cover story, and she was so bitter about his plan to actually marry you, despite the promise of all your money, that she dropped quite a few heavy hints. It was enough to back up our suspicions.'

Caron's lips parted. 'That was another conclusion I jumped to—about you and Kate—wasn't it? And all you were doing was trying to help me,' she muttered. 'So what happened then?'

'Well,' Ewan continued, 'as soon as I could give a date of marriage Gladys went straight to work, even though it was a Saturday morning, and came up with the marriage certificate. From there it was relatively easy to check whether they'd ever divorced.'

'But why didn't you tell me earlier?' wailed Caron. 'I would have just sat tight here.'

'Like I told you in the note you never read?' asked Ewan sardonically.

'You can't expect me to look for things on pillows,' she replied with a trace of asperity. 'I haven't gone in for that sort of thing since I gave up all hope in the tooth fairy.

'Anyway,' she added, 'even when I eventually read your note, after you took me from the church, it still didn't tell me much.'

'Because I didn't want you to get your hopes up in case everything fell through,' explained Ewan. 'Although whatever happened you were not going to marry Neil, even if I had to drag you out of the church kicking and screaming.'

He shrugged. 'Of course, it was just bad luck you not finding that note. I hoped to get back before the ceremony, but I must admit that when I got stuck in that traffic jam on the M25 I really thought the end had come.'

Caron leant back against him and sighed deeply. 'I thought about going to the police,' she admitted. 'But I just thought Dad would be dragged in and Neil would find out and then everything that he'd threatened would just come true.'

His arms closed about her. 'That would never have happened,' he said softly.

'No,' she agreed. 'I realise that now. I acted so stupidly, I might as well have wrapped myself up in a bow for Neil.'

'You know your problem?' said Ewan. 'You just need someone to untie your knots.'

She grasped his roving hands and lifted her face to his, half-laughing, half-gasping. 'This is ridiculous, Ewan Cameron. We have three million things to do if we're going to get this house sorted out before we get married and fly back to Canada.'

'Tenants like a bit of untidiness,' he asserted, pushing her down onto the carpet. 'It'll make them feel at home.'

Sam's taxi pulled up outside the ranch and Ewan handed him a folded bill. 'Keep the change, Sam. Reckon you've earned it.'

Sam looked at him and then at Caron. 'Maybe I could open a dating agency,' he smiled.

'You already have,' replied Ewan. 'You'd be surprised at the number of people who get together simply after pitching up at your saloon.'

Caron watched the car pull away and then turned to Ewan.

'Well, Mrs Cameron,' he demanded softly, 'how does it feel to be home?'

'Nice,' she sighed. 'As good as realising that I didn't have to marry Neil and that my father was completely honest.'

She followed him up the steps, stopping to look at the mountains. 'Weren't we lucky?' she breathed.

He nodded and followed her gaze. 'Yes,' he agreed. 'We were. And now this is just like old times.'

She looked at him and smiled. 'Not quite,' she contradicted him. 'At least I know who I'm staying with this time.'

He dropped the bags and pulled her close. 'You're staying with the man who loves you on this occasion,' he informed her.

She looked at him, her lips parting soundlessly. 'Say that again,' she whispered.

He gazed at her and smiled. 'I love you, Caron Cameron. Always have done, I guess,' he added. 'Ever since you arrived on my doorstep that night and dared me to throw you out.'

Caron grinned happily at him. 'I suppose we really ought to thank Neil for bringing us together.'

He shook his head. 'By the time the police are finished with him he'll be perfectly happy if he never sees either of us again,' he drawled. 'But I'll tell you one thing. There'll be no rushing off to the wilds of anywhere else if we happen to have an argument.'

She gazed at him innocently as he opened the front door. 'What on earth could we have to argue about?'

He lifted her into his arms and headed for the bedroom. 'Housekeeping?' he suggested, booting the door closed behind them.

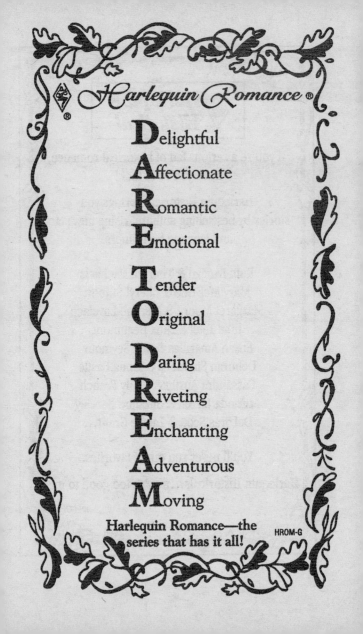

Harlequin Romance ®

Delightful
Affectionate
Romantic
Emotional

Tender
Original

Daring
Riveting
Enchanting
Adventurous
Moving

Harlequin Romance—the
series that has it all!

HROM-G

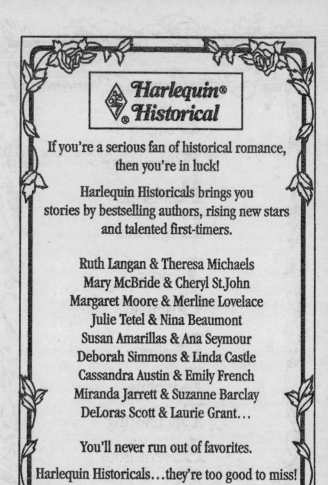

◆ Harlequin®
◆ Historical

If you're a serious fan of historical romance,
then you're in luck!

Harlequin Historicals brings you
stories by bestselling authors, rising new stars
and talented first-timers.

Ruth Langan & Theresa Michaels
Mary McBride & Cheryl St.John
Margaret Moore & Merline Lovelace
Julie Tetel & Nina Beaumont
Susan Amarillas & Ana Seymour
Deborah Simmons & Linda Castle
Cassandra Austin & Emily French
Miranda Jarrett & Suzanne Barclay
DeLoras Scott & Laurie Grant...

You'll never run out of favorites.

Harlequin Historicals...they're too good to miss!

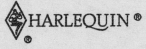

HARLEQUIN PRESENTS®

HARLEQUIN PRESENTS
men you won't be able to resist falling in love with...

HARLEQUIN PRESENTS
women who have feelings just like your own...

HARLEQUIN PRESENTS
powerful passion in exotic international settings...

HARLEQUIN PRESENTS
intense, dramatic stories that will keep you turning
to the very last page...

HARLEQUIN PRESENTS
The world's bestselling romance series!